# When a Husband Is Infertile

# When a Husband Is Infertile

*Options for the Christian Couple*

## Byron C. Calhoun, M.D.

Baker Books

A Division of Baker Book House Co
Grand Rapids, Michigan 49516

Published by Baker Books
a Division of Baker Book House Company
P.O. Box 6287, Grand Rapids, Michigan 49516-6287

Printed in the United States of America

### Cataloging-in-Publication Data

Calhoun, Byron C.
    When a husband is infertile: options for the Christian
couple/Byron C. Calhoun.
        p.   cm.
        ISBN 0-8010-2582-6
    1. Infertility, Male—Religious aspects—Christianity. I. Title.
    RC889.C35        1994
    616.6'92—dc20                                          93-1762

# Contents

Part **1**

# Emotional Perspectives

*Sons are a heritage from the Lord,*
*    children a reward from him.*
*Like arrows in the hands of a warrior*
*    are sons born in one's youth.*
*Blessed is the man*
*    whose quiver is full of them.*
*They will not be put to shame*
*    when they contend with their*
*enemies in the gate.*
                                            *Psalm 127:3–5*

# 1

## Discovering
## the Problem

Numerous books about the woman's odyssey in the realm of infertility exist, but I know of no Christian book that addresses the topic of male infertility.

The Lord's sense of humor in my infertility is extremely wry. I became a doctor of obstetrics and gynecology because I liked to birth babies. My whole life now consists of the rush of delivering God's new creations, but I shall never deliver my own biological child. In this book I will attempt to catalog my wife's and my personal struggle through infertility, particularly my male infertility, and how we believe the Christian can and should respond.

The book grew out of a conversation that my wife, Kathy, and I had one evening after church. We had just arrived home after the Sunday evening service, and I sat on the couch devouring the Sunday paper, that is, the funnies page.

Kathy began, "Byron, did you know that the Smiths had a fertility problem? They have been trying to get pregnant for the last three years."

"So, what have they done so far to see what the problem is?" I answered.

"Nothing, really. They tried to use temperature charts, and she has had a pelvic exam, but no other tests."

"Has he had a semen analysis?"

"Not that I am aware of, but I didn't want to pry too much."

"Since when did you become so shy? You usually ask those questions the first time you meet people!" I teased.

"Byron, that's not fair! It is just that people start talking to me and tell me their problems. Can I help it if it usually gets around to children and fertility problems? They wonder where our children get their red hair, and that leads to the story of our adoptions and our struggle with infertility."

"How come their husbands don't usually talk to me about this stuff? I wish I could share our struggles, particularly mine, with others more effectively. I'm not much into the group therapy idea, but I think it would be interesting to talk about our journey with infertility."

I discovered my low sperm count after we had tried for six months to conceive. Male infertility affects almost five million couples in this country alone.[1] This means that there are 2.5 million males with my problem. We had delayed pregnancy in our marriage for five years until after I finished medical school and my year of internship. I felt that I did not have sufficient time to spend building a marriage and raising a family. If I had known there would be such difficulty having children, I might have done things differently. All I know now is that in Romans 8:28

God promises to work all things for good, and in the end that has proved true for us.

Initially we tried to schedule intercourse around Kathy's midcycle, when her fertility would be greatest. The midcycle is between the eleventh and seventeenth days for most women. We had intercourse every other night starting on day eleven. This allows the sperm count forty-eight hours to recover. Otherwise, with daily intercourse the sperm count may be too low to cause a pregnancy. We did that for two to three months.

Kathy became frustrated, so we tried using a basal body temperature chart. To do this we used a special thermometer from the drugstore that is printed for 97–101 degrees Fahrenheit only. It is broken down into small increments so the temperatures can be read accurately. The woman starts taking her oral temperature each morning after the menstrual flow has ceased. It must be done each morning prior to rising and any activity. The log is kept to determine when the temperature drops below baseline (about one degree). This drop lasts about twenty-four hours and the temperature then rises to about one degree above baseline and stays elevated until either the next menstrual period or pregnancy occurs. If the temperature stays up past the anticipated flow date, a pregnancy test is needed to determine the pregnancy state.

The most fertile time is when the temperature has just dropped and then risen. The egg is thought to be viable for only about forty-eight hours. Sperm live about seventy-two hours. The system seems very fragile, but virtually 90 percent of couples who have unprotected intercourse in one year will conceive.[2]

Kathy went through all the symptoms of depression and mourning when she failed to become pregnant. She became very tense and weepy. At times her frustration took the form of anger not only at not being pregnant but at me and God. She blamed me for our having waited so long and God for not answering her prayers.

There were many nights of tears, especially around her menstrual periods. If I failed to call from work, notice meals or clean clothes, or talk about the day, I met a very unhappy wife. I finally knew that if nothing I did was right when I got home, or if the phone call home was filled with nothing but complaints, she was not pregnant yet.

The pressure to do something became intense. After six months, I finally consented to start the infertility testing process, even though the classic definition of infertility is one year of unprotected intercourse without conception. Kathy acutely felt pressures to enjoy motherhood, since that remained her strong desire. She possessed a prolific family of three siblings, all with three or four children. She felt she had waited in obedience to her husband for five years and now could not understand why God was withholding the precious gift of children from us.

I weathered pressure to perform at the appointed times. Kathy called to tell me it was the right time. I began to feel more like a prize Hereford bull and less like a husband. Intercourse lost a lot of spontaneity and enjoyment. I dare say if we had not been committed Christians, we might well have ended in divorce. It became difficult to communicate about anything without starting an argument about children that ended in accusations. Mostly, I tried to blame Kathy for not taking her temperature right and for putting a lot of pressure on me to have a child.

Maybe children weren't what we wanted after all, I reasoned. Our lifestyle was enjoyable with lots of travel and few cares. I was comfortable. My sinfulness went to such lows as to accuse Kathy of trying to put me in the position of the bad guy for not wanting her to get pregnant. Withdrawal and isolation were my tools to cope with the dawning possibility of my own infertility. Denial also played a significant role in my struggles. I could not believe God would allow me to go through such a time of loneliness. There existed no one in whom I could confide the thought that I might have a problem with infertility. I had no close Christian brothers. My job as a resident in the hospital took up so much time that it left only small amounts of time for leisure. Most of that time I spent on Kathy. Finally, our difficulty with communication kept me from my undeniable suspicion that my physical problem of a varicocele (varicose veins along the tube that conveys semen) might be causing our problem.

At last I gave in to Kathy's pleadings that something must be wrong. We decided I would be tested first, since a semen analysis is the easiest infertility test to perform. Besides, Kathy had very regular menses and no family history of infertility. Her basal body temperature charts all appeared the same, showing nice ovulatory cycles with perfect one-half to one-degree Fahrenheit elevations at midcycle.

The fateful day arrived, and I went to the laboratory technician to obtain the sample. The technician's name was Kathy, too. God has a great sense of humor. She gave me a small, plastic, sterile container and pointed me to the nearest rest room down the hall. Being sent to the rest room to masturbate for a semen analysis is one of the most humiliating experiences in life. One is always afraid someone will walk in and know what is going on in your stall. I obtained the sample with some difficulty and much distaste. It was to be analyzed that day. I went back to work in the obstetrics clinic.

My urologist called me later that day. He told me the news was not good. I only had one million sperm per high-power microscopic field examined. He wanted to know if we had abstained from intercourse for forty-eight to seventy-two hours. I assured him we had. He decided to retest me one more time. The urologist informed me that the sperm structure looked normal but moved abnormally and were decreased in numbers. He wanted to know if I had a varicocele. I admitted I didn't know for sure, since I had never been examined for one.

I could hardly believe my count was only one million per microscopic field, with marginal activity. This number was well below the normal value of 20 million sperm per high-power field, with good motility (ability to move).

I didn't know what to tell Kathy. She knew I was doing the count and would be waiting for the results. I dialed the phone in a bit of a daze and started to talk. "Hi, munchkin, what are you doing?"

"Oh, cleaning out the oven." She paused. "So, Byron, what was the sperm count?"

"Not good, I'm afraid."

"What's wrong?"

"My count and motility are low. I have only a total count of four to five million, which means only one to two sperm per high-power field."

"What does that mean? Are you going to need a biopsy or surgery?"

"Whoa! I need to repeat the sample first and then get an exam from the doctor."

"Well, when will that happen?"

"Remember, we need to wait forty-eight to seventy-two hours to repeat the sample."

"Oh, that's right. That can be by Friday, then."

"I'll talk to you again tonight."

"Wait! Tell me how you're doing."

"All right," I lied. "I'm just glad we've got a probable diagnosis for our problem. I'll talk to you tonight. Love you. Bye."

I repeated the count on Friday, and it was the same. I scheduled an appointment with the doctor for Monday afternoon. We discussed my history, which contributed no source for my low sperm count. He examined me next, doing a thorough genital exam.

"I think you've got a varicocele on the left side that might be the source of your problem. Certainly the count shows good forms with decreased motility and number. The literature suggests that this type of problem is correctable with surgery to remove the varicocele. It is an abdominal procedure that corrects the veinous return to the testicle. The count usually rises slowly over six months and peaks at about two years. I can do the surgery next week."

I gulped and said, "Let me talk it over with my wife."

"All right, but I think you really ought to consider surgery. It might be one of your only chances to get your wife pregnant."

My varicocele was a large collection of veins around the left testicle. They resembled a clump of worms. Such a varicocele can cause infertility in some men by increasing the temperature of the testicle to prevent sperm formation or prevent drainage of the hormones that regulate sperm production. The testicles must be one to two degrees Fahrenheit lower than the rest of the body to produce mature sperm. That is why God placed them in such a vulnerable place outside the body, in an exposed position, for cooling. Sometimes a man's wearing cotton briefs instead of boxer shorts can raise the temperature enough to impede sperm production. Even the hot tub he used three months ago could possibly alter his sperm formation.

It is important to note that just because a man has a varicocele does not mean he will be infertile. That is why a thorough evaluation is important, so that any confounding variables to his male infertility (certain medications, trauma, or history of infection) can be separated out.

What would I tell Kathy this time? I did *not* want surgery. I knew she would be gung ho for anything that might give us a chance at pregnancy. I dialed to call home.

I told Kathy that my examination revealed a varicocele of my left testicle.

"And?" Kathy responded.

"And he wants to do surgery, but—Ithinkweought-toadopt," I gushed.

"Why? Did he say that we couldn't do anything about your count?"

"Not exactly. He said I needed to have surgery for my varicocele."

"What surgery is that?"

"Abdominal surgery to remove the collection of veins from the testicle."

"Why don't we try the surgery?"

"I'm not keen on that. I need to go do rounds. We'll talk more when I get home."

"Don't hang up and be abrupt like that. Does this bother you?"

"Not really," I lied. "I sort of suspected this might be the case."

"Why didn't you tell me before?"

"I didn't think it would be important. We'll talk tonight. Bye."

All the way home my mind was in a whirl. What did I believe about God's loving Son Jesus Christ? When Polycarp was preparing to die a martyr, his accusers agreed to spare his old life of over eighty years if he would recant his faith. What did he believe? He replied, "Am I to deny my Lord who has loved me faithfully all these years? May God forbid!" Didn't I believe as Polycarp? Should I be willing to junk my belief in God because he had thrown this particularly disturbing situation at me? Certainly not! I must allow this obstacle in my path to help mature me and bring me closer to the Lord and my wife.

It seems the only times I start to understand the wealth of goodness God has given me in my wife is when I am confronted with a difficult situation. I present it to my

God-given mate, and she outlines the perfect solution. It is so aggravating! (God has great fun in these situations.) The lessons in learning about God's sufficiency never end. I arrived home and we continued the conversation over dinner.

"So," Kathy began,"what are you going to do about the surgery?"

"I don't think I want to do this. I think God wants us to adopt or remain childless."

"When did you start thinking we shouldn't have children? I thought we discussed this and both wanted several children. We didn't agree about no children before at all."

"I think we ought to reconsider how we may have been chosen by God not to have children. After all, if we were supposed to have children, wouldn't God have given them to us?" (This idiotic statement parallels arguments about flying in the early part of the century, when people would say, "If God wanted man to fly he would have given him wings.") "Also, think of how much better we'll be able to minister if we are childless." (By that I meant, I'll able to own a sports car, take long trips, and generally indulge my own selfish desires.)

"But I thought you wanted children. Those are sort of ridiculous reasons for not wanting them," volleyed Kathy a little heatedly.

"They are not ridiculous!" I declared pompously. I really was somewhat afraid of being cut and didn't want the pain of surgery. I was being a physical and spiritual wimp. I know that most men do not relish the thought of someone putting a sharp knife anywhere near their genitalia. It seems foolish, but part of each man's ego is linked to his sexuality. This especially includes his genitals. Perhaps it relates to the line from Isaiah that talks about a male with "crushed testicles" being unable to serve in the Jewish temple. I think it centers viscerally in me on the inability to perform sexually if my genitals are damaged. That is a big ego blow. I do not like physical pain much, either.

"All right, Byron, you have to decide, since it's your surgery and you are the head of our home. I hope you at least pray and think about it some. Remember, the urologist said this might be our only chance to have our own biological children."

True to her word, Kathy did not mention the surgery again. I argued with God about the surgery for about a week. Finally, after much prayer and meditation, I was dragged kicking and screaming by God into agreeing to the surgery. I planned it during my vacation in November 1984. All the preliminaries had transpired in early October, so I had a wonderful month to brood over the surgery, but the time actually went quickly. We told no one at work or in our families of the low sperm count. It had become a thing of shame to me. I had never thought worth resided in the ability to father chidren, but now since I could not propagate my own children, I began to look on them in a new light. I had lived my life fully and vigorously. This was a blow to virility. I had always, as a faithful Christian man, assumed that God would grant me my own biological children.

The day for surgery arrived. They placed me in an ill-fitting, windy gown and left me in a cold, double room. The young man with me was scheduled for an arthroscopy (surgery with a special scope in the knees). He asked me about my surgery. I just told him it was a "male problem." That squelched most of the conversation. I didn't feel much like talking. The anxiety of surgery made me not want to talk. My nervousness before surgery sort of surprised me. After all, I was an M.D. and ought to be used to surgery. But that was other people's surgery, not mine. I had glibly reassured dozens of patients prior to this. Those reassurances sounded hollow to me now that I was about to be on the receiving end. I battled the anxiety by praying and focusing my mind on Psalm 23. The recitation of those calming words in my mind brought me back to a healthy respect for the surgery, but the sweaty-palm fear was gone. I think it is normal to have great anxiety before any surgery, even a relatively minor one. The Lord developed that sympathetic or involuntary part of the nervous system that physically prepares one for the surgery.

Kathy did not come with me. It would have made me more anxious to have my family present. That remains a personal choice. Having others around me in moments of stress drives my anxiety level higher. Other people find a great deal of comfort in relatives staying close by. I could feel Kathy's prayers were with me, and that comforted me a great deal. I, too, prayed God would grant me rapid healing and an increased sperm count.

The time arrived all too soon for me to be wheeled down the hall. I'd walked these halls many times on my way to gynecologic surgery and had often seen the green tile on the walls left over from the 1950s, but they were particularly depressing to me from my gurney. I bravely waved to the surprised operating-room people. They wondered if I was ill, but I reassured them it was an elective surgery. I remained too shy to tell them it was for a low sperm count. One of my favorite nurses was in the surgery room with me. Her name is Jennifer. She, too, had a fertility problem; her husband had a low sperm count. She asked me if it was all right if she helped take care of me, and I said, "Please do." The medical community is protective of its own, and I received VIP treatment.

I had already changed into a gown, so they placed a sheet over my legs and a blanket on my abdomen to keep me warm. Operating rooms are notoriously cold, kept cold because the surgeons wear extra gowns and become very warm if the room gets too hot. I was rolled on my side into a little ball for the spinal anesthesia. I felt the anesthesiologist probe my back for the right spot in my spine for the anesthesia. He cleansed my back with cold iodine solution and draped my back with a sterile towel. The small needle pricked, and the sting of local anesthesia radiated across my back. I could feel him push the needle in. It was an eerie sensation to be able to feel pressure but no pain. They rolled me over on my back. My legs felt very warm. I could feel them but couldn't move them.

They cleansed my abdomen with iodine again, and all the time I prayed the spinal would work effectively so I would not have to go to sleep. I have morbid fear of general anesthesia. I gag easily, and the thought of not waking up is real to me, even if it means being with the Lord. The surgery started out well, and I did great with my prayer until ten minutes before the end. That is when the Lord tested me to the limit. The spinal began to wear off, and the last ten minutes really began to stress me. The surgery was supposed to last about thirty to forty-five minutes, and the anesthesiologist had used a short-acting agent in my spinal. Unfortunately, the surgery went longer than anticipated. I could actually feel them sewing my tissues and muscle coverings together. It hurt so much I wanted to cry out, but they finished quickly. Fortunately, this experience is rare. The only reason the anesthesia wore off is the anesthesiologist tried to be kind and gave me a low-dose spinal. Usually the anesthesiologist will put a patient to sleep if this happens or give large doses of medications. I did not want either. I wanted to be able to go home quickly after surgery. I knew more medications meant a longer stay in the recovery room.

The recovery room was a blur, especially after the morphine injection for pain. I did very well, and went home the same afternoon. The only episode of comic proportion to me was the trip home. Kathy was driving. I had taken a Tylenol with codeine for pain prior to discharge. I did well until one mile from home, when I felt horribly nauseated. I had Kathy stop the car. I proceeded to retch by the side of the road—this with a fresh, tender incision. The Lord was gently reminding me of all the times I had scoffed at patients postoperatively for being such "wimps." Again, it took all my faith and prayer strength to keep myself remembering that God had my good in his interests.

I had planned to use this time of recovery from my minor surgery underneath my 1954 Chevrolet half-ton pickup. I had pulled the rear end and wanted to replace the old leaf springs with some new ones. I just knew the day after surgery I would leap out of bed, blithely waltz down, and start torquing on my socket wrenches to loosen bolts that had thirty years of accumulated rust. Getting sick on the car trip home, the realization that I could barely shuffle to the bathroom, and the fact that I could not straighten up caused me to rethink my goals. By the end of four days I could fasten my belt without feeling I couldn't bear the pain. It took three to four weeks of recovery to get back to where I could bend over without much discomfort. But I had four days of vacation and went right back to work. God was good, and I healed with only a small scar.

The surgery effects are not immediate, and it takes up to six months to get measurable results, after which, hopefully, the counts increase. Then it is up to two years before full improvement is reached. That was hard to keep in mind as I struggled with a sore abdomen. Kathy was a real help at that time. She kept me going and optimistic. She did little things such as help me get up the first few days, bring me things to read, and just leave me alone to mend.

One positive effect of my surgery on me as a physician is that I've become very empathetic toward people with fresh incisions and not so stingy with postoperative pain medication. The surgery helped me to know what it is like to be a patient. Being a patient is a position in which physicians rarely find themselves but are helped to become more sensitive if they do.

# 2

## Coping with the Responses of Others

This chapter is probably the most difficult to write, because I'm trying to accurately record the impressions and thoughts of a while ago. It contains other people's responses to our infertility and how we dealt with them. Most of the remarks were made out of either kindness or awkwardness. Some of the remarks by family were a bit more callous or careless, but we are confident that our families did not mean to hurt us.

The responses of others typically fall into three broad categories. I will discuss several areas of comments and possible replies to each. The three categories can be represented by the following:

1. "There must be some mistake." (denial)
2. "Relax and you'll get pregnant," or "You can always adopt." (pat answers)
3. "There is obviously unconfessed sin in your life, and if you get 'right with God' you'll get pregnant." (air of superiority)

## Denial

The ostrich approach might be a better term for the denial responses to infertility. Family members and friends simply assume the tests are wrong or that the wife will be pregnant soon enough. Either that, or they know of another physician the couple should see for the notorious second opinion. It is as if infertility is a voting procedure or arbitration. But there is no voting on infertility. The chances of victory or getting pregnant do not improve if there are more ballots on one side than the other. It is wise at times to seek a second opinion, but hard data from analysis and lab values are hard to argue about. Most people find fertility so easy they simply ignore the problem and assume anyone who wants will become pregnant. The typical responses were these:

> "Kathy, don't worry. It took us nine months to get pregnant and now we have three children."
> "Just relax, Byron. It's stress that is making you guys have such a hard time getting pregnant."
> "Kathy, I know this great obstetrician-gynecologist who is good with infertility. Maybe he can help."
> "Isn't Byron an Ob/Gyn? Doesn't he have some fertility drugs you can use?"
> "Just have faith, and God will give you a child."

Family members are a bit more touchy to deal with at times. Their denial seems to be in the form of the idea that a family like theirs could not have someone with so obvious a problem in their midst. Since they don't know how to respond, they often simply don't discuss the problem of male infertility itself, or they obliquely express their denial.

The question in every phone call and letter ran, "Are you pregnant yet? We're expecting our third (or fourth) now and we were hoping you might have a child close in age so they can relate better to one another as a family." These well-meaning comments only served to heighten Kathy's obsession with getting pregnant. She often became so distraught that she didn't want to talk to her family.

Other family members looked embarrassed when the subject was broached and always tried to transfer blame to the married person's spouse. It couldn't be their son. It must be that woman he married. My family wanted me to be absolutely sure it was my sperm count that was low and not something wrong with Kathy. They thought we both ought to be checked out. Mostly, though, families in this first category just do not come to grips with infertility. These members often send books on techniques for sex and give advice on how to time intercourse. All of this is most interesting but tends to deny the real physiological problem.

The subtle portion of denial was by relatives who invited us to family activities that included children and then kept up incessant chatter about their families. This area remained very difficult for Kathy. She was expected to have children. But she didn't, and she felt very lonely and frustrated when relatives and friends sat around discussing the latest accomplishments of their children and how much fun they were having with them. Kathy dreaded going to functions with children around or with people with children. In fact no support group exists for spouses of infertile men. There is a national organization for infertile couples called Resolve, but their appeal is mostly to infertile women, not men.

The best response we found to the denial group was to lovingly and patiently explain that there was a real medical problem and what we were pursuing to deal with the situation. For any couples, this can range from an infertility workup, inseminations, adoption, or waiting on the Lord.

The last response seems a bit glib, but Kathy and I are still doing that. I still believe it possible that God may give us a child by a conception of our own someday. Kathy has abandoned that hope of pregnancy, because for her to keep hoping for the chance to enjoy the wonders of having a child inside her womb is painful. She would be wonderfully surprised, but as a partial defense mechanism she has resigned herself to no pregnancies. This is not to say that adopted babies are not your own children. It is merely a matter of position to me. The source of a child is not important. What is important is where they fit into your life. We might be a bit older than usual when we have a pregnancy, but that is all right, too.

## Pat Answers

The second category includes the relaxation counselors. This group believes that simply relieving the pressure of the problem for a while by relaxing will somehow result in a pregnancy. This borders somewhat on what I might call magical thinking—the idea that somehow, by using some sort of relaxation technique, you will be cured and have a pregnancy. There is scientific basis for part of this, since stress is one of the determinants of sperm count. It is thought that chronic stress affects the hypothalamus gland in the brain by suppressing the release of the chemicals that stimulate production of sperm from the brain to the testes (follicle stimulating hormone and luteinizing hormone).[3] However, the use of some sort of yoga-type meditation is not the answer to the stress difficulty. Such meditation involves the use of mantras and chants with mindless repetition. Christians are exhorted to "take every thought captive" and not to pray like the Gentiles who think they will be heard because of their endless repetition. But earnest and sincere prayer to God for peace and trust in any situation is basic to all of life.

The well-meaning relaxation comments are always followed by anecdotal cases of someone who decides to give up getting pregnant and suddenly is pregnant. The typical story is as follows: "John and I tried for five years to get pregnant and had just found a baby when I became ill and went to the doctor. I found out I was two months pregnant, and we didn't adopt the child after all."

Of course, stories like this tore at Kathy's heart. God is sovereign and can do as he wills, but it seems unlikely that simply by relaxing one might get pregnant. I could understand the relaxation if it meant simply placing your trust in God and not worrying about fertility. But conceiving by just relaxing is difficult to believe.

Along with this set of comments come a dozen or so tested remedies from health food stores about vitamins, new drugs to try, exercises, devices to help fertility, and new physicians to consult. It becomes difficult to smile and thank well-meaning people for their input. I became very weary about "new studies in Europe," Vitamin E, and oysters. The most amusing people were those who tried to interest me in devices. There exists on the market for those who have a low sperm count because of a varicocele and resultant increased temperature around the testicles a set of "cooling briefs." These briefs fit like a normal set of cotton briefs except they cool the scrotum to about one to two degrees Fahrenheit below normal temperature by circulating coolant around the scrotum. The idea of wearing such a device around the hospital at work seemed very amusing to me.

I am sure there are some people who might jump at the chance to do anything that will raise their sperm count, but I guess unless there is a large controlled, double-blinded study showing a definite benefit of any of the above suggestions, I remain skeptical. Besides, it is difficult in my work at the hospital to keep changing in and out of scrubs and maintain a set of such cooling briefs in the appropriate configuration. At that point I decided that I could live without such a device and began to seriously consider adoption.

I understand how the reader might be a bit puzzled by our consideration of adoption after only a few months of waiting on the surgery (two actually), but we were trying to open all avenues for the Lord. We were emotionally and spiritually ready to begin the adoption process, and God was ready, too.

Kathy also became weary of hearing from her family that if she and I would stop trying so hard to get pregnant we would have no difficulty. We needed to trust God, and things would work out. This opened a whole new area of doubt for Kathy. She became angry with God at times and could not understand why he should test her so sorely. She did not appreciate what she perceived as her family's testing of her faith. Her family seemed to her to be questioning her ability to trust God for a child, since she could not resign herself to just waiting on the Lord for a pregnancy. She felt at times, though, that the infertility did exhibit a lack of trust in God on our part.

"Why does my family not realize that we have a real problem with your sperm count? Why do they keep telling me to relax?" Kathy asked. "I am relaxed!"

"They just don't understand totally all your emotions. Your folks think if we pray enough you will get pregnant.

It is true God answers prayer, but maybe he wants to answer prayers for us by an adopted baby."

"I know. But my folks seem to believe I am not having enough faith and that is the reason I am not pregnant. They keep telling me about a believer at their chapel who was infertile for years and then got pregnant. They think we ought to wait for God to give us a child."

"I know, and I am willing to forego adoption if you want and try for a little longer to get pregnant."

"I can't stand the waiting sometimes. Besides, we agreed before we were married that we'd like to adopt. I think we should start now. I just wish my folks would see us adopting as a viable option."

"I'm sure they will understand, Kathy. Give them some credit for their own maturity. We need to keep talking to them and praying for them, too. It isn't easy on them to see their daughter and son-in-law suffer. We know that they are praying for us."

The basic response to these well-meaning individuals, again, was to center on the fact that there was a problem, that we did believe in God's sovereignty, and that we wanted to see the methods or techniques written up in a more reputable journal than a health magazine or a women's monthly. It also helped a lot to laugh about the infertility, as in the case of the "freezing briefs."

## Air of Superiority

The hardest and most insidious of all the categories to deal with is the "sin-in-your-life" category. Christians often use this as an explanation of infertility. It takes the most damaging toll of all. It is not enough for most Christian couples to be barren and search their own lives and souls for some unconfessed sin. Well-meaning brothers and sisters probe with personal and hurtful questions at times. They often take the subtle form of "You know God blesses those who are obedient." This implies that, first, because you are not fertile you are not blessed; second, that you are not blessed so, therefore, you are not obedient; and finally, you are obviously in sin because you are not fertile. It is a bit of circular logic that cannot be dealt with as long as you are not pregnant. The lack of pregnancy just serves to prove the not-so-subtle accusers' point. This is because everyone "knows" that bad things only happen to sinful people, which in reality is neither true nor logical. Bad things happen to everyone. But often it seems the wicked have pretty much what they want (something that frequently bothered David in the Psalms). The other side of the "unconfessed sin" illogic is, then, that everyone who does conceive children has no sin, which is absurd. But those biological parents who make the accusation of the infertile couple implicitly set themselves up as being sinless, and, therefore, superior.

This argument of unconfessed sin ignores the whole concept of the sovereignty of God and flies in the face of numerous instances in the Old and New Testaments. We need only look at the trials of Joseph in Egypt to see that a man of God may, through no sin of his own, have vile things happen to him. Joseph was never accused by God of sin, yet he was wrongfully accused by his master's wife and ended up in a stinking prison cell. He used the opportunity for God's glory. Elijah and Elisha were both oppressed for doing good and following God, but they kept on the path and did great things for God. We may observe Job as a vessel whom God allowed the full wrath of Satan to buffet and bruise. Yet, in the end, Job realized that God is sovereign, and does as he wills for our good, and is to be trusted in all circumstances. Elizabeth and Zechariah waited for years to have a child, and when God answered their prayers he sent their son to prepare the way for the Christ. Sarah and Abraham truly had the ultimate fertility problem. They were both over ninety years old before Sarah conceived. (And we thought that six months was a long time!) None of these people were called sinners in Scripture, yet all were in some way oppressed and had their faith tested.

The New Testament is full of the trials of Paul, Peter, and John. Many apostles died violent deaths at the hands of the rulers of their day. These and other examples serve to fortify the Christian believer who has searched his soul for unconfessed sin and found none. We know that adversity is not always a sign of sin. Adversity may be the result of sin in your life, but do not be deceived into the wrong thoughts. Experiencing adversity is not a sure sign of unconfessed sin. This sort of success gospel is damaging not only to infertile couples but to the church as well. God is not a Santa Claus to be manipulated as we see fit. He is not an idol of stone to be appeased with a broken heart. He is the sovereign Lord of the universe and disposes as he wills. And unfailingly, in the end, he shows himself to be a loving God.

This is not to exclude the concept that God may choose to bless people and that he has promised to give us the desires of our heart. God has promised to never leave us or forsake us. He has promised in Romans 8:28 "that in all things God works for the good of them that love him, who have been called according to his purpose." He has not changed. Kathy and I believe that our marriage is much stronger after weathering the infertility storm. We are more empathetic with infertile couples and have had opportunity to minister to several families and couples with our problem. We have, through our adopted children, forged many friendships and intimate relationships which would have been overlooked before. We have been able to use the comments of people about our children to turn things to a spiritual plane. Comments about how much the boys look like brothers may be turned to the idea that they are spiritual brothers or sons of adoption. Small talk about how lovely are their red-blond curls and questions about where they got them have been springboards to talk about God's working in our lives through the adoption of our three little guys and one daughter. We know that children are a gift of God. We have experienced it.

The challenge to the infertile couple is to respond in a biblical manner to Christian brothers and sisters and do it in love. The infertile couple may want to be very certain there is no conscious sin in their lives that will hurt themselves or others and then move onward. They should go to their brothers, sisters, and parents and church elders to have them search out their lives as well. Nothing is as healing as the wounds of a friend (Prov. 27:6). Also, it is important to be patient with fellow believers. The fertile couple will never totally understand the true beauty of having children. It seems that we sons of Adam appreciate only things we must wait for and be denied for a season. Fertile couples can almost be pitied; they have it too easy.

Most of all, remember that family, friends, and the church all love the couple and want to be a comfort. They want to know what they need most. Perhaps one way to end the confusion is to tell others they are needed to listen to the couple, to call and share, pray for them, or just to give them a hug. If we want sensitivity to infertility we need to be sensitive ourselves to others' needs as well. It is unfortunate if the infertile couple become so wrapped up in their own world of pregnancy that they miss opportunities to minister to others.

The final sensitivity we all may gather from infertility is that there are people who are hurting inside, and we may say insensitive things that cut deeper than the knife. It may be a careless comment about divorce to a hurting person, or a judgmental statement about sin to a person who is struggling with some area of temptation. The church must regain its ability to deal with truth in love. It must be the verbal as well as physical healer and encourager.

# 3

## Am I Still a Man?

I will discuss maleness and infertility in this chapter. It contains some insights into how we men think about infertility. I will address the following four areas of the topic:

1. Feared lack of success
2. Perceived loss of virility
3. Shattered myth of invulnerability
4. Loss of normalcy

**Feared Lack of Success**

I especially remember a conversation with my mother when I was in the fifth grade and trying to fit into a new school. We had just moved from Kalispell to Dillon, Montana, and I was having trouble adjusting.

"What's wrong with you today?" my mother asked.

"None of the kids at school will have much to do with me, and they don't want me to play with them on the kickball team."

"Are you worried about that? Are you going to let that bother you? You're better than that, and you can accomplish anything you want. They are just jealous of your grades and other abilities, so they pick on you. Remember, I always felt I could do anything I set my mind to. And you can, too. So, don't let these small-town minds get to you. Go out and beat them at their own game by being better and working harder."

These thoughts fueled my driving ambition. My delusions and egocentricity persisted as I pursued an appointment to the United States Air Force Academy. I won the appointment without much effort and went on to be accepted at medical school as well.

Infertility cannot be solved by hard work. It brought a whole new realization to my life regarding the sovereignty of God. Have any of you in your Christian walk finally realized that you can't truly do anything without God's help? Before I knew of my infertility I mouthed that my sufficiency was from God. I claimed 2 Corinthians 3:4–5: "Such confidence as this is ours through Christ before God. Not that we are competent in ourselves to claim anything for ourselves, but our competence comes from God."

But I didn't really believe that, because I felt that I could do anything as long as I worked hard enough. This is the ultimate in idolatry: to make ourselves out to be like God. I was jolted to discover that I couldn't do much about the infertility except have the surgery and pray that it worked. I couldn't work up a higher sperm count or do some sort of exercise to make me successfully father a child.

## Perceived Loss of Virility

I grew up with the usual midwestern small-town pastime of athletics and the macho, tough-guy attitudes that went with it. I was not a Christian, and being in athletics meant to be accepted socially and affirmed in my maleness and toughness. I lettered in three sports and thought of myself as a virile young man. The time at the Air Force Academy, with its reinforcement of the idea that I was the "cream of the crop," obviously meant that I was a potent young man. How could I not be a virile, potent man and do all those push-ups, long runs, sit-ups, obstacle courses, and pull-ups? I never thought that God would humble me at the academy and bring me to himself. But a time of adversity at the academy would be preparation for one of the most bitter times of my life: facing my infertility. (Ironically, excess exercise actually reduces the semen count because of increased core body temperature.)

## Shattered Myth of Invulnerablity

God had other plans for me besides being a fighter ace and chairman of the joint chiefs of staff. He desired to make me useful for his kingdom. To do that he needed to change my orientation. So he proceeded to get my attention by bringing me to a crisis in my life. Prior to this crisis experience at the academy, I had done whatever I set my mind to and believed I could do everything under my own power. This included my spiritual walk. Not understanding saving grace, I thought God wanted me to merit his favor. The way to heaven for me was to work my way there, and for that I needed a set of rules to be a success spiritually. My life filled with a checklist of meritorious activities. It remained very pharisaical, since I kept a rigid set of rules that I thought God required of a righteous man. I became a self-righteous prig. Because I did not smoke, drink, swear (much), or fornicate, I looked down on those who did. I totally missed the points Christ made about heart attitudes and stayed selfish and judgmental toward others.

God ended this charade and brought me to himself in a unique way. He allowed me, through the loss of my long-time girlfriend, poor academic performance (I wasn't a 4.0 student after all), and sudden loss of my Aunt Gene to come to a personal crisis.

My old girlfriend refused to participate in any religious activity at all, so we parted company my sophomore summer, even though I still was not a Christian. Her grandfather had been an evangelist and drove her mother and her away from God. I still bought the godly life and couldn't be with someone who didn't want God in her life.

Academically, the academy challenged me to the highest limits. I found myself coming up against material I truly needed to work on to master. The first quarter of math covered everything I had learned in four years of high school. The academy flogged me with engineering courses like mechanics, aeronautics, astronautics, statistics, and advanced calculus.

In the midst of grieving for my girlfriend, Aunt Gene died in October 1976. After her death, a big motivator in my life was gone. I had gone to the academy in part because of her input in my life as a female mentor. She represented what I thought a nurse and woman officer ought to be. She influenced me probably most of all to enter medicine. Her caring attitudes and special love for me (she was childless) made me want to honor her even more after her death. It helped ease me into medicine after I lost my pilot qualification because of deterioration of my eyesight.

The cruelest blow to my emotions came when I tried to talk to my old girlfriend about my aunt's death. She refused to really talk to me and sounded as if she didn't care. Perhaps that was misperception on my part. She probably thought I was trying to win her back through sympathy, which was not the case. I knew our previous relationship would never return. I needed someone close to talk about the pain in my heart over my aunt's death. I was struggling with the question of why God would take such a good woman away so early. But the phone call informing me of her death had cut me like a knife, and to this day I have never forgotten it. Yet, as for Joseph in the Book of Genesis, God used it for good. That call became the final blow to my tottering world. My invulnerability was shattered. The call would haunt me until God converted me in January 1977.

I went home on leave in December 1976 confused, weary, and soul sick. I visited Carolyn, a dear friend of the family, who sensed my despair. I talked with her about my loss of Aunt Gene and of my girlfriend.

Carolyn said to me, "You really need to turn these things over to Jesus, Byron. That's what I do when things get too much for me here at home with the kids or Loren. Jesus is my great comfort, and since I've learned to let go and let God work in my life, I am content. I don't worry about the house being messy or the kids being noisy. I let God worry about those things, and I am content."

I mumbled a sort of embarrassed affirmation of her thoughts and wondered what she meant. I had played religious games so long that I knew she had something I lacked but wasn't able to admit it. The remainder of the conversation drifted to small talk. I started to leave, and Carolyn ran upstairs to secure two books.

"Read these, Byron, and maybe they'll help you to find your way better."

I didn't read the titles until I got home. I found she had loaned me two books by Francis Hunter. I hid them from my folks because I was embarrassed to let them see I was reading some "trashy" religious book given to me by that "religious crackpot" friend of mine.

I boarded the flight back to the academy and began reading *Praise the Lord Anyway*, by Francis Hunter. She wrote about real living, and I wanted it. I now understood that I had to "fish or cut bait," as we say in the Midwest. I had to either believe the whole Bible, apply it, or just forget it. I knew I could not just have a set of rules to follow, because I had attempted that route and failed miserably. I finally saw that Christianity consisted not of a set of rules but a relationship with the only begotten Son of God.

So, on January 4, 1977 at 37,000 feet on a United Airlines flight over Denver, Colorado, he brought me to himself in a personal relationship. I felt as John Wesley did, "my heart strangely warmed," and I knew that I did indeed believe! Now I knew that I was not invulnerable, but my sufficiency was from God (2 Cor. 3:5).

## Loss of Normalcy

Following my conversion, I grew spiritually at the academy and ended up being accepted to medical school. Between the academy and medical school I taught junior high school students at the Officers' Christian Fellowship (OCF) in Pennsylvania. I met my wife, Kathy, there and we married a year later.

After I found I could not father children, strange thoughts filled my mind. I must admit I centered on my loss of the normal procreating function. My fellow residents thought it amusing I was infertile. I didn't particularly like the fact that treating infertility was a part of my specialty (gynecology). The patients were too dependent. I became obsessed with checking my sperm count to see if it improved. I read every article I could on drugs to improve counts and on surgical successes. I grew more intense in my residency to make up for my loss of biologic function. Many people might call it a transference of my anxiety or insecurity to my work. All I know is that if you don't have a woodpile to chop on, you use your work as a substitute.

As each month went by and we did not have a pregnancy, the questions surfaced. Why did the drug abuser, unwed teen, and abusive parent have no trouble conceiving while we could not? Kathy cried out to God and became upset over each menstrual period. I became withdrawn and sought the solace of my work. I did not want to discuss it.

The defense mechanisms we build are strong, but God is stronger still. He helped tear down those walls that separated Kathy and me from each other and from him. He also answered the questions of why for us in a very beautiful way.

# 4

## Emotional Consequences of Being Infertile

T he emotional consequences of infertility ravage Christians with their instability. Kathy and I felt like the believer in James 1: 6 "who . . . is like a wave of the sea, blown and tossed by the wind." The ugliness of doubt described in James 1 puts the believer through four basic emotions. I shall describe each in detail and present biblical responses. The emotions are denial, anger, elation, and depression.

### Denial

"Delight yourself in the LORD and he will give you the desires of your heart" (Ps. 37:4).

The Lord does promise to give us the desires of our hearts. Initially Kathy and I pretended that the infertility didn't really exist. I would have the surgery and solve the problem. We dodged questions from friends and relatives and didn't discuss the problem much at home. This is a normal first response. We somehow believed that if we ignored the problem, it would go away. We forgot about God's words in James 1: 3, "that the testing of your faith develops perseverance . . . so that you may be mature and complete, not lacking anything."

Each day we passed in polite conversation and didn't talk about what time of the month it was. We made love with a vengeance at the "right times" but didn't talk much. The denial ritual even went so far as the purchase of infant clothing and cribs in anticipation of the birth of a child. We did not want to be caught at the last minute. We painted the nursery and Kathy stenciled rocking horses around the walls.

Satan uses the denial emotion to numb God's people and prevent them from developing a healthy concept of God's discipline and love. God says in Proverbs 3:11–12: "My son, do not despise the LORD's discipline and do not resent his rebuke, because the LORD disciplines those he loves, as a father the son he delights in." Satan knows if he gets us to deny anything the Lord tries to teach us, he has already laid the seeds of doubt that will invalidate our faith. The doubt is not sin, but the denial of God's purpose is. This does not invalidate the feelings we have. The feelings are real, but our faith is grounded in the Word of God, not in our feelings about the Word. Sometimes all we can do is cling to the promises in God's Word.

## Anger

The denial phase can only last so long. Denial wears thin and is soon replaced by anger with God. Kathy felt this most of all. She could not understand why God allowed "the prosperity of the wicked" (Ps. 73:3). The drug abusers and unwed teens all had children and we had none. Kathy felt like Job 27:6: "I will maintain my righteousness and never let go of it; my conscience will not reproach me as long as I live," and Job 31:35, "I sign now my defense—let the Almighty answer me; let my accuser put his indictment in writing." She felt unfairly put upon by God and wondered why she was being punished. She took the lack of fertility very personally. She did not see that maybe she had nothing to do with the infertility. Patience might be her reward for her dealing with infertility, but it was not sin that kept her from having children.

My anger sat deeply beneath the surface and smoldered. Then it blazed out against uncooperative, abusive, irresponsible patients. I prided myself on my toughness with dealing with unpleasant patients. I had more patients leave the hospital against medical advice than any other resident in my training program, simply because of my rudeness. I disguised it as telling the truth in love, but it remained my childish way of dealing with my anger against God. I came to actually enjoy browbeating patients into leaving the hospital by making their lives unbearable. I subtly drove them out by denying them privileges and punishing them for minor deviations in behavior like walking in the halls without permission. Unrighteous, hidden anger is a terrible thing. That is why the Lord says in Ephesians 4:26, "In your anger do not sin."

The submerged anger also broke out when I lashed out blindly at Kathy. I vented my frustrated anger at her because she was convenient. I thought it was all right to abuse my spouse, since she was there to help me.

Paul continues in Ephesians 4:26–27 that we ought not to let the "sun go down while you are still angry, and do not give the devil a foothold." We both realized that our anger hindered our relationship with God and with each other. I would like to say that we miraculously started treating one another well and gave up the anger, but that would not be true. We did take the words of God to heart and conscientiously did not go to bed until we had worked out our differences. That made sleeping a lot easier and helped defuse a lot of the volcanic emotion. Remember, we talked about instability. With the stress of infertility, the anger often lurked below the surface, and instability became a way of life. We did eventually defeat the devil in this area, though. We learned to accent the anger but deal with it constructively by remaining calm. Admitting the anger does a lot to help the spouse to understand the reaction of anger. I learned to submit to my wife as instructed in Ephesians 5:21 and "love [my wife] just as Christ loved the church and gave himself up for her" (v. 25). Again, the answer to the emotion is to center the thinking on the Word of God.

## Elation

Elation may seem out of place here, but it belongs. The instability swings from anger to very high elation. This emotion occurs when the wife is now a week late to menstruate and might be pregnant. Each day the temperature chart stays up and the menstruation is delayed signals a possible pregnancy. Kathy would clean the house, fix special meals, and be very talkative. I would be guardedly elated. We just knew this time would be different and she would be pregnant. God had at last answered our prayers: "The LORD has heard my cry for mercy; the LORD accepts my prayer" (Ps. 6:9). We would go out to dinner and plan our delivery. I'd argue with Kathy about where we'd deliver and how we'd manage the labor. It was the highest of all highs for an infertile couple. Then the crash.

## Depression

When the menstruation occurred, I often got a tearful phone call to tell me that we had failed again. I always offered next month, but Kathy stayed stricken. She would be weepy, and nothing I offered or said would be helpful. I learned not to bother her much with talk. I certainly learned not to bring up any controversial topics. Kathy described her feelings like being in a fog or a bad dream that you want to awaken from. We never reached clinical depression, but we had lots of lost appetites, poor sleep, loss of energy, listlessness, and fights. Satan used these times to try to get us to doubt that God would do what he said he would. During those times the best defense is a good offense, to continue in the Word and claim the promises in Psalm 37:4: "Delight yourself in the LORD and he will give you the desires of your heart," and in Romans 8:28. Many times that was all Kathy and I could do. We sat holding each other, clinging to God's Word. The emotions washed over us, but we managed to remember that God's Word is forever. The emotions themselves are neither good nor bad. It is how people deal with them that God cares about.

We sin, we seek forgiveness, and we go on. God said in James 1 that the testing is so "that you may be mature." The next chapter will help explain why we had our trials.

# 5

# Maintaining a Strong Marriage While Coping with Infertility

Submit to one another out of reverence for Christ. Wives submit to your husbands as to the Lord. For the husband is the head of the wife as Christ is the head of the church, his body, of which he is the Savior. Now as the church submits to Christ, so also wives should submit to their husbands in everything. Husbands, love your wives, just as Christ loved the church and gave himself up for her to make her holy, cleansing her by the washing with water through the word, and to present her to himself as a radiant church, without stain or wrinkle or any other blemish, but holy and blameless. In this same way, husbands ought to love their wives as their own bodies.

Ephesians 5:21–28

It seems fitting to remind us all of where we must operate in a Christian marriage. With infertility, as with any struggle, we come to see the problem as more important than the relationship. Let me illustrate. As children we all work on letters of the alphabet to form words. We labor over the strokes of the pencil to copy exactly what the teacher draws. We stay absorbed in the mundane drawing of lines until the glorious day when the teacher opens our eyes and we see the relationship that those squiggly lines have to words. Those words then form sentences, which form paragraphs, which make up papers and books. Soon we understand the wisdom of the labor to learn about lines and letters. The struggle is not the essential thing but the relationship that the labor has to the lesson the teacher is trying to show us.

God used the problem of infertility to teach Kathy and me how to build a stronger marriage relationship through that struggle. We needed to learn how to submit to one another. Paul makes the very pointed observation in Ephesians 5:21 that we must submit to one another. That means we place ourselves voluntarily under the authority of one another out of our reverence for Christ, and that husbands ought to be submissive to their wives. I can hear the men saying, "You mean I should submit to my wife and let her run things?" No, that is not what I am saying at all. I am saying the husband ought to take what the wife says into account in all major decisions and problems, including infertility. If she is not pregnant after six months of trying and wants you both to be checked out, the husband should not balk but just get the evaluation done. Maybe she has wisdom he doesn't know about. Besides, if he loves his wife as Paul describes in Ephesians 5:25, he will honor her request.

I can hear the wives saying, "Yeah, preach it, brother!" Before wives get too excited we need to discuss what submitting to a husband means. It does not mean being a servile doormat. It does mean the wife gives valid input and then lets her husband make the final decision. If the husband wants to be silly and ignore her, she can let him do it as long as she is not forced into immorality. Stupid decisions in the family are his responsibility, according to God's Word. But wives ask, "What if he is wrong or very stubborn?" Let him alone. The Lord will deal with him just as he did with me.

I thought I knew best in everything in our marriage. Fortunately, God gave me a real Proverbs 31:26 wife: "She speaks with wisdom, and faithful instruction is on her tongue." Kathy really knows how to get to the root of a problem by asking the right questions. I believe it is a gift of God to women to know how to ask men probing questions that will rattle them out of their smug complacency. Kathy rarely nagged me about getting evaluated when we didn't conceive. She just kept asking me what I thought was wrong. Why was she not getting pregnant? I sort of knew the answer: my varicocele I discussed in an earlier chapter. I just didn't want to face up to the fact that I might be infertile. She demonstrated the godly response. She remained submissive to my authority but showed me the way to submit to her in love.

As a result of her gentle questions, I finally agreed to evaluation and we found our problem. Notice I said *our* problem. An important part of maintaining a strong Ephesians 5 marriage is realizing that to submit to one another is to bear all difficulties together. Nothing pleases the devil more than to divide a couple on a major issue like fertility. Kathy never blamed me for having a physical defect nor belittled me. For the fragile male ego that meant a lot. Husbands and wives *never* blame each other for the problem. It is not something anyone is to blame for. Sometimes, as in our case, the Lord uses infertility to teach a lesson.

Another way to use the Ephesians 5 passage to strengthen the marriage is to allow it to push a couple beyond their marriage. Centering on their own problems with morbid introspection leads only to frustration. If they submit to each other in love, the love then naturally flows outward. Many couples need a break from their children, and offers to baby-sit for weekends are most welcomed. Childless couples can help others strengthen their marriages by providing other couples their badly needed outlets for special time together. It also provides a great opportunity to see if they really have the gift of child care. Nothing sobers the infertile couple more than taking care of two or three children under the age of five, especially if the children are in diapers. Such weekends make infertility seem like a blessing.

You men need creativity to make your wives feel special even without children. Take time for dates once a week or give special little gifts. Continue to court your wife. She was a wife and lover long before she became a mother-in-waiting. Treat her like a mother and remember Mother's Day. She deserves that support, to know you see her as the motherly type.

Wives, you usually possess more creativity than your husbands. Use it. Have surprise dinners, outings, and events. Men do like surprises too. Keep your focus on the marriage, not on your infertility. Children are only one facet of a lovely relationship between a man and woman. Develop those special bonds while the children are not yet present.

Finally, just enjoy the unique time together, because once the munchkins arrive, it will be all over.

Part **2**

# Medical Perspectives

# 6

## Normal Male Reproductive Functioning

This chapter deals with the medical information regarding male infertility. It may seem a bit of a thrash to wade through the material, but it does help in better understanding male infertility.

Infertility is a problem that affects almost 5 million couples, or 10 percent, in this country alone. The ratio of male to female infertility is split almost in half. That means there are about 2.5 million males in the population who are, for all purposes, sterile.[4] We have an incidence of cerebral palsy in this country of one in one thousand births as compared with one in ten males who are infertile. So we see the magnitude of the problem.

The infertility can vary from lack of sperm (azospermia) to counts below the acceptable minimum of 20 million per cubic centimeter (cc) of semen. To discuss the problem well, we need to know what the normal male is like and what the sources of difficulties are.

We will discuss this in two areas: (1) male reproduction, and (2) ways of testing for infertility.

## Male Reproduction

Male fertility is based on the male producing a normal number of sperm in his testicles. Sperm maturation starts in the testicles and is influenced by the presence or absence of hormones or chemicals in the blood that help regulate body functions. The testicle is influenced by the hormones gonadotropin-releasing hormone (GnRH), testosterone, follicle-stimulating hormone (FSH), and luteinizing hormone (LH).

GnRH, FSH, and LH are all released from the pituitary gland in the center of the brain. Gonadotropin-releasing hormone is secreted in a rhythmic pulse under the influence of neurologic and higher hypothalamic hormonal transmitters. Follicle-stimulating hormone is thought to initiate the formation of sperm in the testicles. It provides the initial signal to the testicles to start the immature sperm cell to become a mature cell. In the female it causes the formation of the egg that ovulates. Luteinizing hormone continues the process by helping the sperm go on to maturation.

Testosterone is what makes little boys become men. It supports beard growth, deep voice, muscle bulk development, and secondary sexual differentiation. Testicular type steroids are the drugs the body builders inject to build the bulky muscles they desire. Testosterone is negatively influenced by LH. As LH increases, testosterone decreases. Testosterone supports the development of the prostate gland and seminal vesicles (pouches that temporarily store semen). Both secrete fluid for sperm nourishment when they are ejaculated or released. Testosterone also maintains sex drive. Testosterone levels vary in the day. They are highest in the morning (explains a lot to wives about mornings) and lowest in the evening. Testosterone needs to be free in the blood to do its work, and most of it is bound to proteins to keep its action under control.[5]

The process of spermatogenesis, or sperm production, starts in the special stem cells, or spermatogonia. These primitive sperm cells go through several steps. In one step the number of chromosomes splits to twenty-three through a process called meiosis, or reduction division. These then mature to spermatozoa through a series of changes called spermiogenesis.

The time it takes to accomplish spermiogenesis is unclear, since most of the early stages are not well studied at present. It take about seventy-four days to develop a mature spermatozoa from the iniation of the meiosis. Once the sperm are produced, they must pass through a tube called the epididymis, which takes twelve to twenty-six days. So, the semen analysis that is studied after seventy-two or more hours of abstinence from intercourse is really the result of events that began almost three months before.

The epididymis is also the region where the sperm undergo the chemical and physical changes necessary to become mobile and able to fertilize the egg. Any abnormality in this organ can influence the motility of the sperm. The epididymis empties into the vas deferens, which is the actual tube carrying the sperm to the urethra, or urine tube, for ejaculation. On the way from the prostate gland the vas deferens is joined by the seminal vesicles which together form the ejaculatory ducts that carry the sperm and seminal vesicle fluid through the prostate to the urethra. The prostate has its own opening into the urethra and adds fluids to protect the sperm from the natural acids in the woman's vagina. The prostatic fluid nourishes the sperm on its arduous journey.

Since the prostate has its own opening into the urethra, it is possible to have blocked ejaculatory ducts and still have ejaculation of prostatic fluid without any sperm present.

This process is all in vain if the male is unable to produce an erection to deposit the semen in the vagina. The penis's erection is controlled by the parasympathetic nerves. These are the nerves that normally cause a person to relax. They decrease heart rate, constrict the pupils, and decrease blood pressure. It seems strange that relaxation is crucial in intercourse, but the reason the parasympathetic nerves are involved is that they relax the arterioles that supply blood to the penis. They allow the penis to become engorged with blood and erect. These nerves also cause the bladder neck to close so the sperm do not end up in the bladder instead of the penis. If the parasympathetic nerves are severed, the male is impotent and is unable to fertilize the female through intercourse.

The sympathetic nerves are those nerves that control "flight or fight." They increase heart rate, dilate eyes, and increase blood pressure. The contractions for ejaculation are controlled by the sympathetic nerves. These nerves cause contraction of the smooth muscles in the vas deferens, prostate, and seminal vesicles forcing the sperm into the posterior of the urethra and help close the bladder. If the bladder neck does not close because of some disease such as diabetes or because of a traumatic interruption of the nerve path, the sperm is ejaculated into the bladder.

The fluid the sperm swim in is a complex soup of seminal fluid (from the prostate gland and seminal vesicles), fluid from the Cowper's glands near the prostate, and fluid from the proximal urethra.

The seminal fluid has fructose (simple sugars) and prostatic fluid (zinc and citric acid). This secretion appears to regulate the ability of the sperm to move.[6]

The semen coagulates during ejaculation to keep it in a single mass, which enzymes then cause to liquefy. If the semen does not liquefy, the sperm are stuck in a jelly-like mass and unable to fertilize the egg.

## Ways of Testing for Infertility

The major factor in determining infertility in my case was the semen analysis. Earlier I described my suspicions about my own varicocele and possible infertility with resulting surgery.

Because the easiest test to perform in an infertility workup is the semen analysis, we started there. We know 50 percent of infertility is male, and it is logical to test the male right away. The semen analysis is a simple yet hard-to-interpret lab test. It must be understood if we are to fully appreciate male infertility and part of the trauma a male must go through to be evaluated for his infertility.

The period of abstinence needed to get an accurate analysis varies from two to seven days. Most urologists (urinary tract specialists) suggest a minimum of forty-eight to seventy-two hours. It is necessary to obtain at least two and sometimes more samples to truly prove infertility. The specimen is collected by masturbation in a sterile or clean wide-mouthed cup. This is by no means an easy task for any male and particularly the Christian male who is taught that masturbation is not acceptable. This is part of the denial process for the male. He dreads having to obtain a sample in some drafty, sterile, brightly lit room. It is humiliating enough for him to think he might be the source of the fertility problem, and worse to have to go to some lab to try to get a sample without any of the specialness of intercourse. The taboo on masturbation runs very deep.

In my own practice with infertile patients, obtaining the semen analysis is sometimes a major obstacle to evaluation. If the male has too difficult a time he may have his wife help him. The wife, also, may wish to go into the lab room to assist her spouse with obtaining the sample. In fact, I usually encourage this approach, since it makes the couple feel less inhibited about the problem.

The Lord understands this necessity for the analysis. He does not count it as a sin like Onan's in Genesis 38:8–10 of purposefully and selfishly spilling his seed to prevent his brother's widow from getting pregnant (God's decree for carrying on family lines of inheritance in the Old Testament). Masturbation is a sin when it becomes an obsession.

It is important not to get the sample by withdrawal method, because withdrawal gives a contaminated (non-sterile) sample that may confuse the interpretation of the test. If a man is unable to obtain a sample by masturbation, then there are special polyethylene condoms that can be used with intercourse. Regular condoms should not be used, because they have chemicals to inactivate sperm. The condom is cleansed on the outside and inverted over the collection jar with care taken to save the entire sample. It is important to get the sample to the office or lab within two hours after collection. If it is cold outside, the sample needs to be kept warm next to the body in the sample container. If the sperm are chilled, they will die.

Once at the lab, the sperm is examined for viscosity, motility, live-dead ratio, count, morphology, and chemical composition. The viscosity is rated subjectively as either flowing freely or well liquefied, or viscous and sticking to the test tube.

The motility is evaluated in light of the the proportion of mobile sperm and quality of motility. The sperm are usually scanned at 100X magnification to look for extra cells like bacteria or for clumps of sperm. The percentage of motility is estimated by counting the number of mobile sperm in five to ten fields at 400X magnification. The sperm's quality of motility is based on the rapidity with which the sperm moves forward. It is based on a 1+ to 4+ system with the 4+ being normal motility. A second wet mount of the sperm is done at four hours to see if the motility has changed and to determine if infection is present if the motility has decreased rapidly.

If less than 50 percent of the sperm are motile, a stain is used to see if the sperm are alive and not moving or are dead. The dead sperm take up the special stain and the live do not. This might help reveal a problem with liquefaction in spite of normal sperm count.

The sperm count itself is done with special grids used to count red blood cells. Five squares are counted, and the number of sperm in the five squares is multiplied by one million. A number greater than 20 million per cubic centimeter is normal. We now have computerized microscopes that do mechanized counts on special slides and measure motility by the average time it takes the sperm to move across the grids.

The sperm are examined for normal or abnormal shapes. Abnormal sperm do not swim or fertilize well. Certain genetic defects or physical problems produce abnormal sperm. This might necessitate a blood draw for chromosomes and antibody detection. We will discuss those more fully in the next chapter.

Even if the semen analysis is normal, a definitive test is done to see if the sperm will penetrate the cervical mucous and be able to enter the female reproductive tract. For this reason, the postcoital test (PCT) was developed. The couple has intercourse, and the female visits her gynecologist who aspirates some of the cervical mucous within two hours after intercourse. The lab looks to see if there are any live sperm in the mucous sample. If there are live sperm in the mucous, it is a normal test. If it is abnormal, the couple know that they are probably dealing with a male-female interactional problem (possible antibody problems), and other tests need to be done. If the test is normal, they can be somewhat assured that they have normal reproductive capabilities. The discussion of anti-sperm antibodies is beyond this text. Suffice it to say that if they are suspected, further testing is necessary.

The most invasive tests that might be performed if a man has severe loss of sperm production (oligospermia) or no sperm (azospermia) are testicular biopsies and injection of a special dye to see if the sperm tubes (vas deferens) are open. Dye is injected up the urine tube (urethra) under low-level X rays to see if the dye enters the vas deferens. The thought of someone placing a needle or tube in my testicles did not make me very happy and probably contributed to my lack of enthusiasm to be evaluated for infertility. All I could imagine as part of the workup after semen analysis was a testicular biopsy. Even though I was a physician, understood biopsies, and had done hundreds myself on women, I had no desire to have a biopsy done on me. I didn't care if they used local anesthesia and only took "a tiny bit of tissue." I wanted nothing to do with biopsies. Fortunately, only 14 percent of male infertility requires a testicular biopsy, and biopsy is not a routine part of most male infertility diagnoses.[7] The biopsy is actually quite painless, an outpatient procedure using local anesthetic and a small hollow needle to obtain the sample.

This is by no means an exhaustive discussion of anatomy and infertility. For a workup and further information it is necessary to consult with a urologist, who can address your specific diagnosis and therapy.

Male superiority based merely on the ability to procreate is a typical macho attitude seen in many cultures. Our society is not immune from this perception. Part of this has to do with Western cultures' emphasis on sons to carry on family names, and part has to do with virility linked to procreation. A man who cannot produce children is thought to be inferior and effeminate in some way. He is a man who "shoots blanks" and the butt of many jokes. Christ makes mothers, fathers, brothers, and sisters of all who share His discipleship (Matt. 12:48–50).

Procreation is a miraculous event that is no way related to a man's ability or prowess. It is a demonstration of God's love and creative genius. The complex and arduous journey a single sperm must make to unite with an egg and produce a new life only serves to show how small the involvement of the couple really is. God takes a seemingly impossible system and makes fertilization work exquisitely. Therefore where is the boasting? It is nonsense that a man can only be a man when he produces biological children. We need to appreciate this fact as we minister to the infertile and deal with the self-doubt many men have.

# 7

## Problems Leading to Infertility

Most husbands and their wives are blissfully ignorant of the male reproductive system. It is indeed an ingeniously wrought system by our Creator. It seems almost too convoluted to work, yet it functions almost flawlessly. Over 90 percent of couples who desire to conceive will do so in the first year. Over the next two to three years only a small percentage will remain infertile.

It is no wonder with all the complexity of the system that male infertility has such a mystique and is not the usual topic of polite table conversation. Most men, like me, are loathe to discuss infertility with their doctors, let alone their wives.

The causes of infertility are varied and can be divided into the following categories:

1. Anatomic factors
2. Hormonal factors
3. Genetic factors
4. Inflammatory problems
5. Autoimmune disorders
6. Medications
7. Mechanical damage
8. Sexual dysfunction

## Anatomic Factors

Anatomic factors include the varicocele, which is what my problem turned out to be. It is thought to impede fertility by allowing increased heat in the affected testicle. Spermicidal metabolic toxins might build up as a result of impaired drainage in the affected veins. A varicocele functions much like a varicose vein in the leg. It prevents adequate circulation through the testicles.

Congenital anomalies like abnormal urethral openings (too high or low on the penis) may contribute to infertility by not allowing the sperm to enter the vagina. If the opening to the penis is incorrect, the semen merely exits the penis outside the vagina.

The man may have absence or blockage of the sperm tube (vas deferens) and be unable to transport sperm from the testicles to the urethra. The absence of a vas deferens might be the result of a birth defect or injury. The blockage might result in a collection of sperm called a spermatocele. This often becomes a mass in the testicles.

## Hormonal Factors

Hormonal factors, like gigantism or dwarfism, are influenced by excessive levels of gonadotropin-releasing hormone (GnRH) which cause either excessive or diminished growth. This hormone normally pulsates in secretion, but if it is secreted at levels that are either too high or too low, the production of sperm is stopped. Thyroid disease is related to sperm production in that either an increase or decrease in the thyroid hormones affects the production of sperm by inhibiting maturation. The hyperthyroid person has increased body temperature, and this may be spermacidal in itself.

Adrenal disease may cause infertility. It decreases sperm production when the testicles respond to low corticosteroids (secretions of the adrenal gland). This may cause an increased temperature in the testicles and a decreased sperm count. Pituitary problems may cause infertility by producing low levels of the precursor hormones necessary for sperm production. If the LH and FSH levels are too low, the sperm do not develop properly, resulting in abnormal shapes and decreased numbers of sperm.

Abnormal use of testosterone by the precursor cells does not allow the sperm to develop normally, which leads to sterility.

### Genetic Factors

These include Klinefelter's syndrome. Extra or deleted chromosomes may cause sterility due to increased testosterone or abnormal genitalia. Symptoms are two X and one Y chromosome, greater-than-average height, eunuchoid body type (feminine), and long arms. It has an incidence at birth of one in four hundred, and about 10 percent of males with aspermia are Klinefelter's.[8] The main problem is that the testicles are just masses of scar tissue and small in size.

### Inflammatory Problems

Inflammatory responses by the body to mumps, tuberculosis, syphilis, and bacteria may cause infertility. Essentially, any time the body is attacked by an organism, the body will seek to rid itself of the infection by causing a fever with local (on-site) infiltration of white cells. These white cells cause local-tissue destruction in an attempt to rid the body of the sickness. The mumps virus has a special predilection for the adult male testicles and may cause severe swelling of the testicles with subsequent scarring. Tuberculosis is hard for the body to fight, since it hides in the host cells. Its extensive destruction of local tissue can lead to blockage of the sperm tubes (epididymis). Syphilis causes destruction similar to tuberculosis.

The prostate, seminal vesicles, and urethra may all have bacterial infections that will cause inflammation leading to scarring and obstruction.

## Autoimmune Disorders

There are numerous diseases in which the body attacks itself. These are called autoimmune disorders, diseases such as lupus, rheumatoid arthritis, and numerous others. They cause the body to produce antibodies or chemicals in the male's own body that will kill or inactivate the sperm.

## Medications

About 15 percent of commonly used medicinal drugs may interfere with reproductive function.[9] A decrease in the libido may occur if the patient uses sedatives, tranquilizers or hypnotics (Valium-like). Other drugs such as the tricyclic antidepressants (amitriptyline, doxepin, imipramine, cyclobenzaprine) may change libido and cause testicular swelling.

Methyldopa hydrochloride use for high blood pressure may decrease libido in a dose-related fashion and prevent ejaculation. Other drugs that prevent ejaculation include monoamine oxidase inhibitors (for depression) and guanethidine (for high blood pressure).

Antiandrogenic drugs (antimale action) like medroxy-progesterone and spironolactone (for blood pressure) decrease libido. Clonidine (for high blood pressure) causes impotence in up to 20 percent of men. The phenothiazines (for psychiatric use) may be linked to inability to ejaculate.

Certain anticancer drugs destroy the ability of the testes to make sperm, as do heavy metals such as lead or aniline dyes. Sources of radiation such as high-dose X ray for cancer therapy or high-dose microwaves (not ovens) from radar cause low counts.

### Mechanical Damage

Damage to the testicles by blunt trauma, torsion (cord leading to testicle becomes twisted), or surgery may all lead to low counts. Most of the mechanical trauma ends up either destroying the testicles or the sperm tubes.

If the husband had a high fever, enjoyed a hot jacuzzi bath or a sauna, these, too, could affect the sperm count by increasing the testicular temperature. Remember, these events all affect the sperm count three months in advance because the maturation process takes that long to complete.

### Sexual Dysfunction

Too frequent or little intercourse may lead to problems with conception. Too frequent episodes of intercourse decrease the sperm count to levels that prevent fertilization. Infrequent intercourse may miss the fertile time of the cycle.

Vagismis or vaginal spasms may not allow intercourse to take place.

Painful intercourse may prevent couples from engaging in intercourse.

Sexual intercourse with premature ejaculation may place semen outside the vagina.

This is not an exhaustive discussion of all the problems leading to male infertility but should give an idea of the multitude of problems that may arise.

# 8

## Intervention

The treatment of male infertility remains notoriously ineffective, but we will discuss seven areas of possible therapy to increase the likelihood of conception:

1. Abnormal sperm: medication
2. Abnormal hormone levels: therapies
3. Retrograde ejaculation or lack of emission
4. General measures
5. Surgical measures
6. Husband insemination
7. Miscellaneous

### Abnormal Sperm: Medication

Those patients who have idiopathic oligospermia (no known cause for decreased sperm count) might be helped by the use of medications like cortisone acetate, 2.5 mg four times a day, and clomiphene citrate, 5 mg daily for twelve weeks.[10] Others recommend 50 mg of clomiphene for sixty to ninety days.[11] This has resulted in pregnancies in 20 percent of couples. Paulson recommended 25 mg daily for twenty-five days, then rest for five days.[12] This continued six to twelve months. The pregnancy rate was 41 percent. Unfortunately, these rates of pregnancy are not statistically different from the rates over a year with no treatment.

Schachter found that 1 gram of arginine (amino acid) improved the sperm count in 65 percent of patients.[13] Hendry and Schellen recommend mesterolone, 75–100 mg per day for one year, with improvement in counts of over 50 percent.[14] The pregnancy rates in these groups were not noticeably different from those in the control groups.

Low motility has been treated by using human chorionic gonadotropin (HCG): 10,000 units given by injection twice a week for three months.[15] Hendry had similar results with fluoxymesterone, 5 mg per day for three to six months.[16] The patients with low volumes of semen have been treated with human chorionic gonadotropin, 2000–4000 units by injection twice a week for eight weeks. Those patients with excessive volumes(> 4–5 ccs) should use withdrawal after the first ejaculation, since this contains most of the sperm. Too high semen volumes dilute the sperm count and prevent fertilization.

## Abnormal Hormone Levels: Therapies

If the patient has low thyroid tests he needs thyroid replacement, and this often solves the problem. If the patient has low testosterone levels, androgen therapy replaces the low production. Excessive androgens with hyperadrenalism require high dose steroid therapy to suppress the adrenal. If urinary FSH is low, the patient may receive weekly HCG injections of 2000–4000 units twice a week. The other alternative now is a GnRH pump to stimulate FSH production. A small needle is placed in the skin and the hormone is pumped in a pulsating fashion.

## Retrograde Ejaculation or Lack of Emission

In this problem the male's semen fails to be released from the penis to the vagina. Due to a spinal injury, diabetes, or muscular dystrophy the male's urethral sphincter fails to close. Hence, when the man ejaculates, the semen and sperm are propelled backward into the bladder. This makes fertilization slightly difficult!

To solve this problem, a patient has intercourse or masturbates to ejaculation. The patient then urinates into a sterile cup or has a sterile catheter placed immediately. If he urinates into a cup, because the sperm are heavier than the urine, the sperm are recovered by centrifuging the urine. If a sterile catheter is used, sterile saline is placed in the bladder and used to wash the sperm out. After carefully washing the sperm to remove contaminates, the sperm may be placed in the vagina near the cervix for attempted fertilization. Another option is to wash the sperm clean of all semen and place the sperm directly into the uterus as a "sperm pellet."

A technique that may help if the sympathetic nerves to the urethral sphincter are damaged is to give ephedrine (50 to 75 mg), one-half hour before coitus. This may allow the urethral sphincter to close and send the sperm out through the penile meatus.

## General Measures

Sexual technique needs close discussion. Some couples have intercourse too frequently. Forty-eight to seventy-two hours of rest between intercourse episodes are necessary to allow the sperm counts to increase. Otherwise, the count may be too low to accommodate fertilization. The couple also needs to know when the most fertile time in the menstrual cycle occurs. This is accomplished most often by using basal body temperature charts and looking for the temperature drop. The other option is to use the higher technological ovulation kits presently on the market, which may be purchased in any pharmacy. The kits are good but expensive, running about thirty to fifty dollars per cycle. They operate by using color changes of first morning urines to indicate ovulation.

Some couples prefer to use lubricants, but they should be careful to avoid lubricants that are spermicidal. Positions for intercourse that have the female in the superior position or allow the semen to exit the vagina should also be avoided.

If nonliquefaction of the sperm is a problem, the woman should place a suppository of 5 mg of alpha amylase powder in the vagina immediately after intercourse.[17]

Alcohol consumption should be stopped, since it decreases count as well as libido. The male needs to stop wearing tight briefs and switch to boxer shorts to help improve spermatogenesis by decreasing temperature.

Testosterone may be injected in doses of 50 mg three times a week for four to five months to get complete azospermia. After the treatment is stopped a rebound may occur, and an improved sperm count may be seen in 30 percent of men. Five per cent might be made worse, however.[18]

## Surgical Measures

These include repair of the vas deferens by a procedure called a vasostomy using microsurgical technology. Success runs to 90 percent by sperm count, but the pregnancy rates are about 50 percent.[19]

When azospermia (no sperm) is the problem, then sometimes an operation called the epididymovasostomy may be attempted. It essentially opens the epididymis into the vas deferens. It is successful only in those males with a normal testicular biopsy showing spermatogenesis.

Varicoceles may be treated by ligation (tying) of the spermatic vein at the internal inguinal ring. Pregnancy results in about 50 percent of couples.[20]

## Husband Insemination

Some couples may choose, as we did, husband artificial insemination, which concentrates the husband's sperm to increase the count to acceptable levels and then used to inseminate the wife. The semen is obtained by masturbation and placed in a sterile cup. The count is checked under the microscope. The sterile sample is washed with special media in a sterile test tube and centrifuged to remove the seminal fluid. The sample undergoes two washings. A sterile plastic cannula (tube) is used to place the sample into the wife's cervix (uterine opening). The tube advances into the uterus (and may cause cramping in the wife). The sample is then injected directly into the uterus by using a syringe. The average number of cycles needed to get pregnant is about six. It has a very high success rate for men with borderline count and good motility. Kathy and I did this for two months before my surgery, and then another four months before we finally quit and decided to adopt.

## Miscellaneous

Use of any noxious drugs should be stopped. These include all the previously mentioned drugs as well as any illicit drugs.

Antisperm antibodies may be present in the female. These may be treated by use of condoms by the male for six months to a year. Condoms prevent the wife being exposed to her husband's sperm and decrease the level of antibody titers. Conception rates may then be as high as 50 percent.[21] Other therapies to treat sperm antibodies have included infusions of husband's washed white cells. These remain controversial and not accepted as standard care. More information is needed to document their utility.

I mention ovulation induction only to condemn its use in women who are ovulatory without drugs. Some people feel that they ought to ovulate the female partner to provide optimal success for the husband inseminations. This is not standard care and not well researched.

Part **3**

# Christian
# Perspectives

# 9

## Infertility and God's Covenants

What does all this mean to the Christian male? The Scriptures are quite clear that any eunuch or man with crushed testicles could not serve in the temple of the Lord and was to remain outside the temple's inner courts. The words of the Lord in Leviticus 21:18–20 are very explicit:

> No man who has any defect may come near: no man who is blind or lame, disfigured or deformed; no man with a crippled foot or hand, or who is hunchbacked or dwarfed, or who has any eye defect, or who has festering or running sores or damaged testicles.

The man who was emasculated might not "enter the assembly of the LORD" (Deut. 23:1). A Levite could not serve in the temple, nor could a priestly man serve at the altar if he had suffered injury to his testicles. These verses mean little to most people, and are just shrugged off as part of the Old Testament law regarding the temple, pertinent to another dispensation. And we have the great gift of Christ Jesus who made it possible for all people with defects, spiritual or physical, to approach God.

The Old Testament laws are important, however, to understand God's covenants with men. For the promises of God to operate in the Old Testament there had to be a means to pass on the promises God gave. The only way to do that in the Jewish culture was to pass on the inheritance to the sons. Daughters might also hold an equal share, as did the daughters of Zelophehad of Manasseh under Moses in Numbers 27:1–10 and Numbers 36:2. The promises were passed on to the succeeding generations through the birth of offspring. If a man had no children, his inheritance was lost to his nearest relatives, and the promises of the land passed away from him. Christians do not have a specific land in which they dwell, but they still have a spiritual inheritance in their children. This helps understand the seriousness of the inability to bear or father children.

By grasping the concept of heredity we can better understand how many Christian men become trapped and depressed by their inability to father children. The whole social fabric of Western civilization used to hinge on the ideas of male inheritance. The eldest sons in English common law received the inheritances. Only males could become rulers in places like Germany. The kings were warriors, and only males were involved in warfare throughout most of the Middle Ages and beyond. To insure the throne for a ruling family there must be sons and many of them. Childhood mortality was extreme; up to 50 percent mortality of children under two years of age was not uncommon. Whole empires and nations divided by such things as rightful heirs.

The modern Christian male continues to live in a society that places real value on the ability to father children, despite its claims to the contrary. Most people in our society feel the only way to achieve some element of immortality is to have children. Couples resort to using children to give meaning to their materialistic lives. Career women as well as many men find the rosy picture of self-actualization through their jobs is not all it is painted to be. Men find they face questions in their lives they can't answer and hope by giving new life to find the answers to their hearts' searching. Those with low self-esteem believe they will raise it through their children.

Many people pour their lives into their children (usually two: one child unit for each parent unit). It becomes a crisis to those who cannot bear children, and the same people who tear about the business world or professional world with a vengeance start the same intense process to produce a child. They seem to think their sheer efforts can somehow produce a child. This madness spills over into the Christian's world, and Christian couples start to falter and give in to the craziness of pregnancy at any price.

Added to this for many Christians is the emphasis on family life with its perceived spiritual basis in most churches. The Christian male feels a tremendous burden to perform his husbandly duties, and when he cannot, he can suffer real torment. Much of the hurt is subtle, but some is overt. It is very difficult for people to relate to someone who "shoots blanks," as it is termed. Social gatherings become excruciatingly painful at times, because people want to know "when you're going to have children." For me came a unique added burden. After all, I am an obstetrician-gynecologist and I am supposed to lead the way in fertility.

One particular incident stands out in my memory as typical of certain responses to our problem. One of the residents who was a year ahead of me had Rh negative blood, and so does Kathy. He found out I had a low sperm count and very callously told me, "I'll be happy to help you out and inseminate your wife!" He was not noted for his tact and said this in jest, but it did bother me a bit. He had two children and was the department "macho man." I usually got along quite well with him, but that made me a bit angry. I forgave him, though, because even though he was an honorable man, he was a rank pagan. I suppose we should not be surprised at such responses from the world. I think the best thing to remember is that the world will respond inappropriately, sometimes painfully for us, so we can be prepared for it. It helped me most of all to remember God had control of the situation.

The man of God, along with all men who have low counts either secondary to injury, illness, medicines, or physical defect, is a target for all sorts of crude jokes and snide comments. Medicine is professional, but the rudeness exists there as well, as illustrated by my colleague.

The Scripture verses in Leviticus strongly move the man of God as he struggles with societal pressures as well as theological implications. Does this mean that the infertile man cannot serve in the church? Does it mean that he is cursed? Should he be considered as an elder, since he has no family against which to test him as Paul in I Timothy suggests? Does it mean this man should not marry and make his wife barren as part of his "curse"? Why would God torment a faithful man with infertility?

These thoughts and others like them crowded into my mind when we learned of my low sperm count. God is gracious in his Word and does actually answer these questions. The answers were not evident to me initially, and I am grateful that God was patient. He finally sent me to the Old Testament passages in Isaiah 53 that foretold Christ's coming and the fulfillment of the law. Here I saw the picture of the suffering servant in the Lord Jesus. I saw that the foretold Christ "took up our infirmities and carried our sorrows" (Isa. 53:4). This meant that I had a Savior who would bear my burdens with me and heal my sorrow of infertility. There is an ache in the heart of the man who realizes he will not be able to father children of his own. He cries out with Abraham at the prospect of others such as Eliezer of Damascus inheriting his house (Gen. 15:2). Yet, the Lord sent his only Son to make his life "a guilt offering" that would "suffer in his soul" and "justify many" (Isa. 53:10,11). The pure weight of that sacrifice helped me tremendously to know how much God loved me and that he would not leave me alone to bear my burden. It also pointed me to Isaiah 56:2–5, which helped me see what the Scriptures meant with regard to the cursings and blessings associated with children:

> Blessed is the man who does this,
> the man who holds fast,
> who keeps the Sabbath without desecrating it,
> and keeps his hand from doing any evil.

> Let no foreigner who has bound himself to the LORD say,
> "The LORD will surely exclude me from his people."
> And let not any eunuch complain,
> "I am only a dry tree."

> For this is what the LORD says:

> "To the eunuchs who keep my Sabbaths,
> who choose what pleases me
> and hold fast to my covenant—
> to them I will give within my temple and its walls
> a memorial and a name
> better than sons and daughters;
> I will give them an everlasting name
> that will not be cut off."

I began to see that being in a category with a eunuch was not necessarily a curse to me. I saw the healing work of the Lord Jesus Christ and the lack of importance that should have been attached to the mere ability to father children. If God could raise up an army before Ezekiel from dry bones, think what he could do in my life right now with my infertility problem. I began to see what the real practical implications of my situation were. Here God had placed me in the middle of the most technologically advanced society with its ability to do wonders with modern medicine, and it could do nothing to help me. I began to be truly liberated from the bondage of unbelief. I soon learned to expect miracles. This testing of my faith allowed me to delve into the Scriptures and really understand that Christ had died for me.

Kathy struggled with this, however. She told me, "How can I believe that God loves me when he won't let us have children, which is the strongest desire of my heart?"

"I don't have a pat answer for that, Kathy. I know it would sound good to quote from Romans 8:28 and tell you that everything will be fine, but that is glib. I guess that I just cling to the idea of a God who is what he says he is and that he has done marvelous things so far in our lives. He saved me out of my former sins, and for that deliverance alone I would be grateful, even if he did nothing else for me."

"I know all that with my brain, but my heart isn't listening, Byron."

"Then I think we need to pray that God will grant you peace and allow your mind to be at rest, and we know then the emotions will follow. God or I don't make you feel any certain way, but we can help you perhaps see how he does love you and me."

"I don't think I can pray that," said Kathy dully.

"I'll do it, then. You can pray after me if you like. Father-God, I thank you for the lovely wife you've given me and her desire and sensitivity for children. I pray that even now you are answering our prayer for a child. We know you love us and will do only those things that are for our good and in your love. In Jesus' name we pray. Amen."

Little did we know how that prayer would be answered for us. I knew from Isaiah 56 that I had an inheritance in God's kingdom no matter what the status of my ability to beget children, and that became very comforting. I also saw that the curse I lived under could be turned into a blessing with a "memorial and a name better than sons and daughters" (Isa. 56:5). Armed with this knowledge I pushed into the New Testament and found a wealth of assurance of my blessings from God.

The Old Testament passages became understandable in light of Christ's teachings about the inheritance of the blessings in Israel. He taught that the Jews as legitimate children of the covenant would be replaced by sons of adoption, the Gentiles (Eph. 1:5–6). Paul says in Romans 11:17–20 that we are grafted into the true olive tree, Christ, and are sons of God. Israel, because of their apostasy, had forfeited their share as legitimate sons and daughters in the inheritance in God's kingdom. This idea became truly liberating to me. Here I could see that, yes, there once may have been a curse on barrenness but that God could choose to use even a grafted olive branch in his work. Here Paul listed further proof from the New Testament that confirmed Isaiah's thoughts about the validity of blessings showered on the eunuch. He could be blessed with his own inheritance of sons and daughters through the grafted-in branches of adopted children. So the barren couple could experience the gift of having a "blessed quiverful" of children.

I did not find Scripture to deal directly with the concept of male infertility and how it ought to affect a person's choice of lifestyle. In my instance, I did not know about my infertility prior to our marriage and so did not know I had made my wife barren by my low sperm count. I certainly believe that the woman a man plans to marry needs to know if he knows, that this is his state, and likewise, if she knows she is infertile she needs to tell him. Most times, however, this situation is unknown. It is still probably a good idea for a couple to discuss adoption with their future spouses should God move their hearts in this area or they have difficulty as we did.

If infertility is known, it must be dealt with prior to a marriage just as must be the number of children expected in a marriage. The infertile male must deal realistically with the ability to adopt children and the cost and limitations involved. Most agencies only allow a couple to adopt one or two healthy infants. Most have age and income restrictions. The courts will want assurance of their ability to care for a child.

The questions raised above are why I suggest a thorough physical examination for both partners prior to marriage. A woman with irregular menstruation and a history in her family of difficulty conceiving ought to be very frank with her fiancé in the area of reproduction. It might save a lot of heartache later.

Scripture also gives no guideline for an infertile man as to whether he ought to remain single or marry. It is a question that should not be entered into lightly, because, in effect, he makes his wife barren if he marries her knowing he has no sperm, or azospermia, or just has a low count like me. Barrenness is never examined in Scripture as to whether it is male or female, although in most of the references we see regarding infertility it is stated that a certain female was barren. When the infertility is lifted, it is always stated that the Lord opened the womb and she conceived. The argument from silence on male infertility is not a strong one. But since pregnancy is obvious fertility, and testing for male infertility was unknown and impossible, it would appear that all infertility was female

in Old Testament times. To the person who does not investigate male infertility, a conception of any kind must
appear as the woman's womb being opened. However, it
could also be that all those women were infertile and had
their infertility ended by the gracious God we all serve. It
seems that over and over again God used people with a
long history of infertility to do great things.

We may look at the example of Abraham. His wife Sarah
remained barren for a long time (almost ninety years) yet
a great nation came from her. God is not limited by circumstances or physical disability. He is able to go beyond
that infirmity. There is the example of Hannah, who had
Samuel after a long period of barrenness. That greatest
judge of Israel was born only after his mother's time of
waiting on God to open her barren womb. John the Baptist came after a long time of praying and faithfulness by
Zechariah and Elizabeth. Often there seems to be a blessing in the lack of children as people are given time to
mature. These saints of scripture never altered their
lifestyles and had ministries in spite of their being without children.

In spite of his lack of progeny, Abraham remained the
head of his household and a greatly respected leader and
patriarch, even before he had any children. In fact, Abraham's unfaithfulness was to God's promise in Genesis
15:5, where God told him that his descendents would be
as "the stars." Sarah apparently nagged Abraham into sex
with her maiden, and Hagar conceived Ishmael. Then
Sarah conceived Isaac at ninety years of age, according to
God's promise (Gen. 21:2). Ishmael was sent away because
he was the son of a slave woman and not the heir from
Abraham's wife. For generations enmity existed between
the Ishmaelites (illegitimate children) and the Hebrews
(true sons).

Hannah remained a godly woman. She worshiped in
the tabernacle and endured with another wife, a fruitful

one, in a normal Jewish household without her own children. Zechariah served in the house of the Lord as a priest. His priestly duties were not denied him as a result of his wife's barrenness. The Jews of that time did not believe a man could not minister just because he did not have children. The key to Zechariah's ministry became his faithfulness to God's word in his deeds. Zechariah was born a priest and could fulfill the duties as a birthright. We have no such concept in Christianity. One is not born into a specific duty. Yet, the Christian male can still be used in the body of Christ. He may exercise the gifts of the Spirit in charity, teaching, preaching, exhorting, helping, administration, and speaking of tongues (1 Cor. 12:7–11; 27–30).

# 10

## Infertility and Church Leadership

Not all faithful men are fertile. Neither does God punish a faithful man with infertility. However, faithfulness does not negate the effects of all previous sins. If a man did a lot of hard drugs, had alcoholism in his past, or suffers from chronic male genital infection from previous sexual sins, these actions carry into the future. That has nothing to do with God's marvelous forgiveness of sin, but shows and reminds us of the orderly world in which we live and that actions have consequences. To better understand this idea we need only refer to David, who was a "man after God's own heart" yet committed the vilest of sins in adultery and murder. Nathan assured him of God's forgiveness but also told David the sin would have two consequences: the death of Bathsheba's child and that the sword would never depart from his house (2 Sam. 12:10). David's sexual sin plagued Israel and wrought much destruction and despair. Yet, God remained faithful to his covenant and brought a Savior through that very line that sinned so grossly.

God might use a man's infertility to minister to his wife, friends, brothers and sisters in the Lord, and people at work. The vulnerability of male infertility may open new areas of frank discussion between spouses. Perhaps the wife does not share her husband's enthusiasm for children, and God is using the opportunity for them to explore the possibility of remaining childless to better serve him in another ministry. Maybe this provides the incentive to go to the mission field and not feel pressed about family needs or pregnancy.

Perhaps the Christian couple will be able to better minister to a couple known to one of them at work going through a pregnancy loss, for both have experienced loss. Each month without a pregnancy is a mini-loss, and grieving takes place. Christian support to other childless couples during their time of grief in a kind and loving empathy might make all the difference in a witness to them.

There is a great need in the body of Christ for couples committed to the Lord and not busy with their own families. In their churches they might be better able to help singles and childless couples fit into the church ministries and activities by treating them as their surrogate families.

In the historical sense the priests and Levites were all married men. A measure of a man's ability to lead rested on his ability to control his family. If his chidren were disobedient, he led the way in discipline, even including "stoning them unto death" (Deut. 21:18–21). The early church thought so much of this issue of family control and church leadership that they made it an implicit requirement in Paul's letters to Timothy and Titus. The man with infertility, if he chooses to remain single, cannot be affirmed for leadership based on family control if he has no family. Yet Zechariah remained a priest and fulfilled his priestly duties even though he had no offspring until the birth of his son John the Baptist.

The issue is thorny but needs to be analyzed in the light of Old Testament covenant and New Testament fulfillments. The curses of barrenness in the Old Testament (Deut. 28:18–19) related to the land and the inheritance of the land for the Jews. Without heirs, a man was a withered branch whose inheritance was lost forever. His name would be blotted out of the genealogy. This was disastrous for the Jew whose identity remained tied to the land. His name remained preserved through his offspring. As he aged, the elderly, childless Jew had no one to protect him in time of trouble. There was no Social Security. One can well imagine the city-gates business discussions at the elders' seat. A man taking a "quiver" (seven husky boys) with him to help settle disputes would have more power than a man without sons. No one argues with an army. If you have no support, it is quite easy to be ignored. The Jewish man without issue lost his inheritance forever and had decreased influence in his community.

It became easy for the Jews, and some modern Christian males, to extrapolate that if barrenness is a curse it comes on only those who deserve a curse, so obviously there must be some area of unexplained sin in the Old Testament believer's life or in the Christian's life. He wonders if he removes that one missed sin in his life that then the Lord will surely bless him with children, almost as if he can manipulate God into giving him his own way. But this confuses the male Christian, because he knows that not everything that happens is the result of unconfessed sin. Some things are the result of merely living in this sin-filled world, and bad things may happen to good people. Yet, he personally struggles with Psalm 37:4: "Delight yourself in the LORD and he will give you the desires of your heart." They desperately desire a child.

Kathy and I desired a child. "Byron, why do you think that God is not giving us a child? Is there some area of our life that needs to be examined or some sin that needs to be dealt with for us to get pregnant?"

"I don't know, Kathy. We are Christians. Our sins are already forgiven and we are not going to be punished for them."

So, we prayed that God would give us the desire of our hearts.

"But if God loves us and wants us to have the desires of our hearts, why is he not giving us a child? That is our fervent desire, isn't it?" Kathy asked.

"Maybe I am a bit to blame for that. I don't know if the strongest desire of my heart is to have a child."

"What do you mean? I thought you wanted a baby," replied Kathy.

"I do, but it is not the leading desire of my life."

"I don't understand that, Byron!"

"Well, what I mean is having a child is not the reason I live. I have other things like medicine, my residency, and my wife that are more important than a child. I don't need a baby to be fulfilled."

"But I don't have all those things, and I do get lonely at times. My whole desire as a godly woman is to have a godly family."

"You already have that with me. We have a godly home. It doesn't require that we have a baby to have a full home."

"I know that in my head, but it is not easy to validate in my heart. I just can't throw out my emotions."

"I understand that, too, but we need to center on the God who has so graciously provided us with what we already have in our health and salvation. Besides, perhaps God has allowed this infertility to let us adopt and provide homes for homeless children."

Why did God not give us a child? Sometimes God will give a glorious answer as he has in our lives with the gift of four lovely adopted children. But at the onset of our problem, we could not have dreamed the extent of the blessing or the amazing way in which he would fulfill our desires beyond our wildest expectations. He may choose to have other Christians suffer longer or more acutely than we did. Aslan says it well in *The Horse and His Boy* in the Narnia series by C.S. Lewis. "'Child,' said the Lion, 'I am telling you your story, not hers. No one is told any story but their own.'"[22]

The answer for the Christian man is not to despair and be resigned to his lot but to implore the God of heaven to relent and bless him with his abundant mercy. God may give not biological children but sons and daughters of adoption. He may shower his love and give a miracle baby. He may choose to do neither. But we know that all he does ultimately is out of love for those who love him.

# 11

## Infertility and Christian Ethics

At first the news was good; the sperm count was getting better and had gone from a total of 4 million sperm (one per hpf in 4 cc's) to a total count of 16–20 million (4 per hpf). The motility had also increased to 4+ with 75–80 per cent of the sperm in that range. But that was still not good enough to get Kathy pregnant. We needed 20 million sperm per hpf (60–80 million total sperm in 4 cc's).

At this time in 1984 exciting advances were being made in treating male infertility that included husband artificial inseminations (HAI). We decided to try it. This consisted of taking my semen sample, washing it in special media, and spinning it down. The sperm were washed twice to get rid of the semen and leave a "sperm pellet."

Sperm are washed because the semen contains chemicals called prostaglandins that can cause a woman to go into anaphylactic shock if they are injected into the uterus. The pellet provides an easy way to concentrate sperm. The pellet is resuspended in another medium, and a small, soft, plastic catheter is run through the cervix into the uterus. The sperm then bypass the cervix and are sent on their journey with a special boost. We used special ovulation kits to tell us when Kathy was fertile, and she was inseminated every other day for about a week around her fertile time.

This method, we were told, would get most women pregnant by about six months. We went into the insemination business with a vengeance. I would get the basal body temperature charts from Kathy, check the ovulation kits, and then take her to my gynecology clinic to inseminate. But she still didn't get pregnant. Kathy got more and more depressed. The catheter caused Kathy cramping, and she felt cheated.

"Byron, I am really tired of the insemination business. I thought I would get pregnant. I hate the cramping with the catheter. What's wrong?"

"I don't think anything is wrong. It normally takes about six months to get a result with our count."

"I know that, but I thought with our count we'd do better. I don't think this is a very romantic way to have babies." Kathy did not like the fact we were trying to make babies with a plastic syringe. That somehow did not fit the romantic image of conceiving a baby together.

There were other options for us to explore at this point. After eighteen months without noticeable improvement in my count, my urologist tried to get me to try other drugs. One such drug is called clomiphene citrate, which is given to women who have trouble making eggs or ovulating. The drug is not cheap at almost one dollar a pill. It needs to be taken every day and requires about three months to have an effect. Many studies do not show a definite benefit to its use. We were tired of the infertility business. We felt that eighteen months for us without improvement was enough, and we were not about to go into treatments which were at best experimental and of no known value.

How far each couple will go in infertility therapy varies. Some couples feel they must exhaust every avenue, and others, like us, tire of the business and opt for a little more rapid means although not necessarily less traumatic.

What about artificial inseminations? Should a Christian use a donor and have his wife artificially inseminated? The Bible seems to discourage this, and in fact, Onan was punished for "spilling his seed." This was an instance in Israel, however, where the husband was dead and the pregnancy with his sister-in-law was to preserve his brother's inheritance and bloodline in Israel. There could be no inheritance in Israel without a child. The wife would lose her rights if she had no one to protect her. A child protected the widow because it gave her the land rights she needed to support herself and her family. The only avenues open to a childless widow was to marry a brother of her dead husband or become a prostitute if the brother refused to marry or inseminate her. This insemination was not for mere procreation or self-actualization through children. It secured the widow's legal status to stay on the land. Onan did not want a pregnancy by his brother's widow because that would mean less inheritance for him.

Does this mean if I die that my brother-in-law ought to inseminate my wife? I think not. The Jewish insemination was to assure an inheritance in the land, and we no longer need that. Our inheritance is in heaven, as Paul points out in Colossians 3:23–25.

I believe that artificial inseminations with donor semen are a form of adultery. Scripture shows that as long as both spouses are alive we should honor God's requirements of no adultery. Hannah with Samuel and Elizabeth and Zechariah with John both point out the benefit of waiting on God. Abraham's disaster with Hagar was the result of his and Sarah's wavering faith in God's promise and impatience in waiting for its fulfillment.

There is no scriptural prohibition against insemination but it needs to be thought out carefully. Donor insemination amounts to technical adultery, because you take the semen of a man not the wife's husband and use it to conceive. Kathy and I also considered the unavoidable unknowns about a donor, but the heaviest thought of all that nagged us was the idea of adultery. Each couple must choose about donor insemination, but the thoughts about adultery must be dealt with, or there will be future guilt and recriminations. One solution some couples use is to mix the donor and husband semen so the couple doesn't know which sperm impregnates the wife. This might assuage some consciences. But Kathy and I chose not to inseminate by donor.

These are all legitimate areas of concern for the infertile couple. Yet, I believe God would not condone any of these things. God does not want children to be conceived outside of marriage. In fact, when men turn to fleshly methods to circumvent God, as Abraham did with Hagar, we see that God is not thwarted. They only create a worse situation. This means that the use of sperm banks, surrogate mothers, and illegal adoptions are surely not acceptable for the mature Christian trying to do God's will.

# 12

## Adoption

Adoption was a bit of a foreign concept to the Jews, because they kept their family names and inheritances of the land based on their tribal assignments. Christ modified the land concept when he did away with the Year of Jubilee by opening up the spiritual inheritance of the Jews to the Gentiles. Originally every fiftieth year was the Year of Jubilee, when all land reverted to its original owners. Land could never be sold permanently (Lev. 25:8–17); it was returned to the family it had come from during the Year of Jubilee.

Because Christ did away with the sacrificial system and became our final sacrifice, and because he did away with land inheritance and based our inheritance on our relationship with him, we are all now adopted into the family of God as grafted members of Christ (Rom. 11:11–23).

The children God adopts into his spiritual family—all Christians—are his legitimate heirs, something we see symbolized by our adoption of children into our Christian homes.

As my own situation became clearer, I struggled with the idea of adoption. At this point Kathy confronted me with the idea of pursuing an adoption even as our infertility evaluation and treatment went forth.

"Byron, what do you think about starting to go for an adoption while we are working on our infertility?"

"I don't know. I think I am open to it, but I guess I never gave it that much serious thought. I suppose I could live with the idea of raising a child that was not from my own loins."

"Seriously, I'd like to look into adoption."

"Okay. You get the materials, and I'll read about it," I replied without enthusiasm.

I should have known that since Kathy is such a bundle of bustling activity, I would soon have all the information I could handle along with a running commentary on what it all meant. That is her great strength, her organizational ability.

Part of the reason infertility never entered my thoughts early in our marriage was that I figured we could always adopt a child or two or even six. This was naive on my part, not very well informed, and at that point not a truly serious consideration. As we realized my count might not improve significantly and that the average time for adoption is several years, it became a very serious consideration, and we decided to pursue adoption as soon as possible. Even as we were waiting for my sperm count to improve after the surgery, we were trying to find a baby. As we went further into the adoption process we became somewhat despondent, however, and wondered how we could ever afford or obtain a baby. A resident's salary is not outstanding, and we felt the cost might prevent us from having a child. Most private agencies charge from $3500 to $10,000 for the adoption of a normal infant. Even foreign adoptions cost several thousand dollars once you go through all the requirements to obtain a child.

"I looked up the cost of a private adoption here in Missouri, and it runs from free at the state agency with a five-to-seven-year wait, to $6,000 to $10,000 with a private agency and a six-month-to-one-year wait," Kathy reported.

"That's outrageous! I can't believe that! That is almost like legalized black-market babies. It doesn't cost that much for prenatal care, and certainly the lawyer fees and court costs can't be that high."

"I know, and I told you we should have started sooner! We'll never get a baby in this state, because we can't live here long enough since you have to go somewhere else for your subspecialty training."

"Wait a minute! Don't blame me just because there is a long waiting period."

"I know I shouldn't, but we would have known sooner if you had let us try to get pregnant earlier. Now we won't get a baby."

"Do you believe that? You don't think that if God wants us to have baby, that we won't conceive next month or get a baby? We just need to start seriously pursuing it."

"Will you tell everyone at work we are looking for a baby? Let the residents and staff know we'd like to get an infant."

"I will, and we'll look at some more agencies."

Denominationalism is also difficult to deal with at times. Certain denominations have infants but only adopt them out to people in their denomination. That seems fair, except that at times an infant's interest might be better served in a household of a different denomination. Also, not all denominations have an adoption agency to help couples and unwed mothers in their churches. Following is a sample conversation with one agency.

"Hello, I am Byron Calhoun, and we are looking into adopting an infant. We have a fertility problem in that I have a low sperm count. We were wondering if your waiting list is open and how long a wait there might be."

"Are either of you a member of this denomination?"

"No, but I was baptized in your denomination as an infant."

"Well, then you are still one of our denomination."

"No, ma'am. I go to the Presbyterian church now."

"I don't care. Once you have been baptized in our faith, that is it. You are just a nonpracticing member and in rebellion to our denomination. We do have two waiting lists: one for our denomination and one for those outside our denomination. We would consider you a member in poor standing, so at this time we can't place a child with you."

"Oh, I see. Well, thank you for the information."

Most denominational adoption agencies function this way, although most have only one waiting list for their church members. I am not faulting them, because they minister to a tremendous number of people, but I think we might move away from the denominationalism a bit.

Even the hard-to-place child, such as a blind, deaf, or otherwise handicapped child, may be difficult to adopt in some areas. We even checked into biracial adoptions with the governmental agencies, and most of them were reluctant to consider us as parents for a black child. They thought a biracial child in a white family would not be well accepted. The problem is that half-black and half-white children are not readily accepted by black families.

Both denominationalism and the expense of adoption give an edge to the couple with money and in the right denomination. People with lower incomes or in the wrong denomination are on those points barred from adopting.

This smacks of legalizing the buying of babies by excluding the financially disadvantaged and creating the worst sort of religious bigotry.

To thoroughly discuss the crisis of healthy adoptable babies is to enter another whole book. This controversial area of our society deals with sperm banks, inseminations, surrogate mothers, abortion, in-vitro fertilization (IVF), and the refusal of young unwed mothers to relinquish their children in spite of their inability to care for them.

"Kathy, I can't believe they sent this baby home with a drug-abusing mother! We can't even get a baby, and they send these kids home to get abused. How many times have I heard about admissions of children to pediatrics who are abused and neglected? What is society doing for this? Why don't they take those kids away to start with? Why do they have to wait until the child is abused before they can move on these people?"

"I feel the same way. It gets depressing. They have to consider parental rights. It is a fine line."

"It just doesn't seem fair to the babies or us. I sometimes wonder what God has in store for us. I guess we have to trust him with those babies and our infertility. But I am getting tired of taking care of those noncompliant, noncaring women who abuse their babies before they are born!"

"Maybe we can adopt one?"

"They won't relinquish, because as long as the baby is theirs they get welfare and have control of the infant. It can be used against the father and grandparents. It is sad."

"It's true, Byron, that down through history we haven't been very good about protecting or valuing children. When you can't have any you start to see how precious they really are. That's why Jesus wanted them to come unto him."

"I think most of our friends value their children very highly."

"Yes, but they are not as acutely tuned to the value of all children. They can have them any time they want."

"I guess that is true, too. But I don't know of any Christian couples in our acquaintance who don't love their little ones more than their own lives."

Currently we are seeing a new flood of drug-affected, abused, and neglected children. Most counties and states are increasingly crying for people to take these infants off their hands. The breakdown provides us all opportunities to minister in a special way through adoption.

It breaks my heart to think about all the young mothers who take babies home and have no idea how to care for them or support themselves except on public assistance. It is tragic to watch drug-sick mothers who have abused their children in the womb go home with their children. Women who use drugs can cause brain hemorrhages, bowel and bladder damage, loss of limbs, blindness, and agonies of drug withdrawal in their unborn babies. There is growing concern about fetus abuse, but much remains to be done under the law.

I have seen mothers who have lost two to four children to state agencies for neglect and child abuse take home beautiful babies and bring them back black and blue to the hospital emergency room because state laws most often prevent taking a child away presumptively without actual abuse. These children deserve better than this. I am not trying to tout adoption as a cure-all, but many of these children could have safe, stable, and happy homes if we would step in and make ourselves as responsible for our country's children as we seem to be for our homosexuals, pedophiles, and others with equal protection under the law.

After the emotional and physical exhaustion of my surgery had passed, and we had decided to pursue adoption as a possible alternative, we entered into this experience without much knowledge and assumed an adoption would be easy to obtain. We did not realize that the abortion crisis and young mothers keeping their infants had decimated the ranks of adoptable American infants. We found, much to our dismay, that our state's adoption waiting list was about seven years long. We did not have that kind of time to wait, since I was already in my second year of training and only had about two and one-half years left until we moved to another state for subspecialty training.

We turned to private sources and became even more discouraged as we found waits of about two years and expenses in the range of $6,000 to $10,000. We could not afford that kind of money. So we began to investigate independent adoption, using only a lawyer and the adoptive mother.

This forging ahead with adoption raised serious questions in both of our families. Kathy's parents thought we ought to wait and be more patient for a biological child. Kathy was not interested much more in patience.

"I think we ought to get started now, Byron," said Kathy. "I have looked at the various home study people, and it is going to take some time to get things going. The state list for doing a home study is one to two years. The private agency in town will do the home study but wants about $600 up front first. They also want to meet us about three times to check out our home environment and ask a few questions."

"What are they going to ask? I'll bet they ask whether or not we will spank our children. You know we will have to answer truthfully that we believe corporal punishment in limited doses can be very therapeutic for young bottoms."

"I know, and I am also worried about questions about church and whether we will make our children conform to our religious standards. We believe children deserve to be in church at a very young age and be brought to the Lord as soon as possible."

"I know that, Kathy. I still wish that I had not had to live nineteen years as an unbeliever, but it's not for me to question the Lord."

"So, do you want me to set up an appointment?"

"Let's look around and see if we can get a cheaper alternative or a less biased evaluator. I am afraid that we might not pass a secular evaluation. Oh, well. God is in control, and I know if he wants us to have a baby, nothing in this earth will stop him."

This clashed with Kathy's parents' fervent prayer for us to have a biological child of our own. Her parents still pray this prayer, and perhaps they will be rewarded for this faith. We know that Abraham and Sarah waited a long time for their own child through which we have the Lord Jesus.

My own family of nonbelievers also remained less than enthusiastic. We talked about adopting almost any child we could find. This did not set well with my parents.

My conversation with them began after we called them one Saturday evening.

"Hi, Mom, what's new there in Arizona?"

"Nothing much. How's the work going? Are you delivering a lot of babies?"

"Always. There never seems to be a shortage of them around here. Kathy and I want to tell you something and see what your reaction is."

"Oh . . ." came the long pause.

"We want to adopt a baby and still continue the infertility workup. We'd like to get started now on adoption because it takes so long here in Missouri."

"Don't you think that is kind of silly? You are not going to adopt a foreign baby, are you?"

"We've thought about that, too, but no; we're going to try to get a healthy Caucasian baby first, although we feel all babies deserve a home of their own."

"I think that is kind of stupid."

I bristled a bit. "Why do you say that?"

"Well, you know that you might get some child with a mental illness or some sort of major defect, and where would you be? You don't have time in your busy career for a handicapped child."

"Mom, what if we had one of our own that was handicapped? Then what?"

"I just think it is stupid."

"Stupid because you don't agree with it, right? You taught me to think critically, and now that I don't agree with you, I am wrong."

"Not exactly. Why don't you talk to your father."

"Hi, Dad."

"Son, what is this nonsense about adopting a baby? Don't you think you have enough going on right now? I think this is kind of stupid, too."

"Dad, it is Kathy's and my life. We believe God will honor our request and won't burden us with more than we can bear."

"There you go again spouting that religious stuff. Have you been talking to Kathy's folks again?"

"No, Dad, this is what we believe and try to live out. Just trust us to do the right things, huh? Bye for now."

My parents continued to worry about some sort of psychological or emotional illness in the adopted child's family throughout the adoption process. We pointed out that some of those things could be part of a baby that came from our own flesh. They remained skeptical about adoption for quite a while. But after meeting our three sons they think their grandchildren are great. They even think we might be all right in having their new granddaughter.

The pressure from family when we decided to adopt so early after the surgery was significant. Most believed we should give the surgery time to work its effects. I tended to side with them. Kathy, however, would not be stopped in her efforts to seek other alternatives. She felt a baby was a baby and it did not matter whose genes it had. Kathy just wanted the opportunity to raise godly children. I suppose I must grudgingly agree God did bless Kathy's pushing.

Into our house swooped a blizzard of information on adoptions in Missouri. It ranged from international to local. We discovered quickly how little we knew about the law. Fortunately, some friends who had recently adopted knew of a Christian lawyer who helped us get things done quite amazingly.

Still, the thoughts of whether this was the appropriate alternative kept surfacing in my mind. I could not shake off the arguments presented earlier regarding children. I had a great deal of difficulty dealing with the fact I was a eunuch of sorts. I did not have the loss of my virility, but the effects were the same. I could not procreate my species. That still remained a bitter pill to swallow and kept me halfheartedly going along with Kathy. I could not admit to myself that I would be so shallow as to be jealous of those who had no trouble with conception. Yet, neither could I become one of the neurotic people who want a conception at any price as a sign of my masculinity or humanity.

The struggle continued through the winter months from November to January. I remained pessimistic about ever obtaining an infant. We learned that we needed a home study to be considered for an adoption. A home study consists of an individual coming to your home for several visits to see how you live and what your home is like. It includes questions regarding your moral and ethical upbringing. It touches on the subject of discipline. Kathy and I became distraught because we knew we agreed with corporal punishment. Unfortunately, some of the state and private agencies do not. They also tend to be a bit hostile toward the Christian faith. Our preliminary discussions were with people who thought we should not push our ideas of religion onto our children. They thought we should let them make their own choices. We found this to be patent nonsense. Our Lord told us we are to make disciples, and this includes our children first of all.

The preliminary discussion discouraged us quite a lot. We found that it would take about $600 to $750 to get the study completed. There was a waiting list of one to two years to get a home study done without charge by the state. The state people controlled the adoption process by delaying the home study, because there could be no adoption until the home study was completed. So, if a child was found, he or she would have to remain in the custody of the state in foster care until the home study was completed.

To help avoid this long delay and expense, we decided to discuss the possibilities of an independent, private adoption. This meant that in Missouri we could adopt a child legally as long as the birth mother relinquished her rights and the court would allow us to obtain custody of the child. The laws change and vary, so you need to check your own state adoption laws. This Missouri law would help us sidestep the state agencies and, hopefully, speed up the process.

The most amazing part of all this is that God can do anything he wishes, and not even the bureaucratic state can stop him! We first had one opportunity to adopt a girl infant that did not work out but prepared us later for our sons. Almost four months to the day from my surgery we had a call at home about a little red-haired boy who had just been born to a young lady. She decided it would be best to place him for adoption. She was a college student who had denied her pregnancy and went to an emergency room with abdominal pain which turned out to be labor. This denial of pregnancy probably saved Paul's life, since his mother did not have the opportunity to consider an abortion. I immediately called our lawyer, who began the contacting process. He knew we did not have a home study, yet needed one. We contacted the state personnel, who stalled since they were excluded from the adoption. The private agencies in town would not do the home study, either, since they would only get the home study fee but not the adoption fee.

Furthermore, the state would not take custody of the child in foster care as they were supposed to. This was relayed to the judge and juvenile authorities. The judge wrote a court order to place our son in the custody of our Christian friends who had given us the lawyer's name. They were approved, since they had just completed an adoption and had an approved home study. The judge approved a pastor friend to do our home study for us, and we had our little son, Paul Byron, home in two weeks.

Our lawyer was truly amazed. God had worked to foil every bureaucratic trick and uncooperation. He had merely used the law to help one of his children win a victory. Our lawyer said he had never handled such an unusual case in that it went so smoothly. God is so awesome and good!

We had much rejoicing about the adoption. It helped strengthen Kathy's faith immensely. All my doubts about an adopted child left when I saw that precious little bundle with his red hair and sweet smile. I realized when I saw that baby boy that it no longer mattered to me that he was not my biological child. He was my gift from God no matter where he came from.

Kathy remained ecstatic, and the remainder of the legal process went smoothly.

We then waited about eighteen months and began to think about another child. The Lord dropped into our laps our fantastic second child. The story behind his materialization is as unbelievable as Paul's. We had talked to a pediatrician friend of mine about a single divorced lady who was thinking of giving up her child fathered by her boyfriend. She was considering it since she had one toddler at home from her previous marriage and felt unable to handle any more children because of her emotional and financial status. She also had been adopted and had had a wonderful experience through it. She wanted her baby to have the opportunity to have two parents in a warm family atmosphere.

I ignored the information at first but then reconsidered. I withheld the information from Kathy to keep her from getting her hopes up. She seemed to have Holt International Adoption Agency material in front of me most of the time or at least some adoption materials. I heard about the young lady again from one of the residents. She had been scanned and had a little girl. I asked the resident if she had made any plans regarding adoption of the infant, and the resident said no. She apparently was waiting for God to bring the right people. She was a Roman Catholic Christian and had a strong faith, though she did not mind the baby going into a Protestant home. I was overwhelmed! She had to have a repeat Caesarean section since she had a previous birth anomaly that required a repair of her rectum and she could not risk damaging that with a vaginal delivery.

I contacted the lawyer and told Kathy. She went wild. She even went out and bought some lovely, lacy clothes for our baby girl. I was the chief resident on obstetrics that month and helped do all C-sections. It was God's great grace that allowed me to assist at the birth of my second— you guessed it—son. The ultrasound had been difficult and had missed Daniel. No Anna, but a strong little guy weighing only five pounds, one ounce. Kathy was a bit disappointed about another "him" but could return the clothes. She realized she could use this as an excuse for another child, a girl maybe, and so have the larger family she desired. One of the most amazing things about it all is that Daniel has the most lovely red hair, too! Paul and he look so much alike that people mistake them for biological brothers. It is great fun to see the looks of incredulous surprise as we matter-of-factly tell people (if appropriate) that they are our sons of adoption from the Lord.

Joshua arrived by a slightly different route. We lived in Oregon for my training in high-risk obstetrics (maternal-fetal medicine). The two boys were four and almost three when we decided to pursue another adoption. We felt this time God wanted us to seek a hard-to-place or medical-risk infant. We contacted the state agency and met the worker. She initially remained skeptical until she observed our commitment and family. With her wholehearted support we pored over the lists of children. We preferred an infant. There were none at that time, but our eyes caught the story of a little boy born twenty-four weeks prematurely who appeared to need a family. He had been in foster care for over eighteen months and badly needed a home. We went to meet Joshua and fell in love with this shy little towhead. He joined us in October 1987. He is only six weeks younger than Daniel but smaller since he was born so prematurely. He weighed one pound, 13 ounces at birth.

Joshua came to us badly delayed in his development. He was at only nine months of development when he was twenty-two months old. He could not walk, drink from a cup, feed himself, or talk well. A year later he functioned as a normal child. God certainly blessed us in him.

Our last child, Faith, came to us by a circuitous route. We moved to Mississippi the summer of 1989 to begin my payback to the Air Force at Biloxi, Mississippi. Our friends called us in October about a little girl born to a mother who wanted to relinquish her baby, since the baby was conceived by an adulterous affair. The previous adoptive family bowed out when the infant needed special care because of severely poor muscle tone. Faith initially needed a tube in her stomach (gastrostomy) to help her eat, since she had a poor suck, and she remained floppy with poor tone. Her battery of tests revealed no source for this, although she carries a possible diagnosis of Prader-Willi syndrome, which is characterized by poor muscle tone, voracious appetite as children, and possible learning disabilities. God blessed us with this sweet little girl who no longer needs the gastrostomy and now eats all her food orally. She improves daily, after having spent twelve weeks in the hospital and two weeks in intensive care. We wait on the Lord.

The best part of the whole story is that both our families think we have the best little children. All the misgivings about adoption appear to be gone. They do worry about Faith. We think our children are wonderful and always will cherish the special way God showed his love to us through his great gifts.

# 13

## Epilogue

"Thanks be to God who always leads us in [triumph]," says Paul in 2 Corinthians 2:14. I do not say this in an offhand manner nor mean to appear insincere, believe me. If we trust God, he will satisfy our needs.

God allowed Kathy and me to struggle almost one year without conceiving a child before he was gracious enough to send us our first son through the work of good friends and a Christian lawyer. In the midst of our battle with infertility and inseminations God affirmed his faithfulness in a very lovely way. He sent us a beautiful red-haired boy whom we named Paul Byron after my grandfather and my father.

Even if God had chosen to delay a child or not send one at all, he would still be my good Father. We still believed the Lord could send us a biological child and continued the inseminations for another six months after Paul's arrival. But then that became less important as our other children arrived and we began to perceive a different purpose for us.

That does not mean we have forgotten our earlier struggles. We need to understand the nature of God to enable us to live our lives in a consistent manner. It is hard to follow and trust a leader we know nothing about. It is difficult to follow the right path if we don't know the trails.

We must learn that Job's observations about God are correct: God is sovereign and does as he wills, and we are to trust him in whatever circumstances he places us. This is what Job learned and his friends had not understood.

Isaiah speaks of the clay and the potter in Isaiah 45:9. How can a pot know what it is made for? God does as he wills in our lives. As we begin to see his plan unfold, we can say with Paul in Romans 8:28 that "we know that in all things God works for the good of those who love him, who have been called according to his purpose." Then we see in verse 29 that his purpose is for us to be "conformed to the likeness of his Son" and be glorified in him (v. 30). In our Christian parenting, Kathy and I seek to be like him, and this is our goal for our children too. And we see more and more clearly that God's greatest evidence of his love for humans is the fact that he saved us out of our sins for no other reason than that he loves us.

This is not to say that remnants of our pain do not recur. They do. But I now have a better grip on the biblical promise that even eunuchs "will have a memorial and name better than sons and daughters; I will give them an everlasting name that will not be cut off" (Isa. 56:5).

Christian men, even though you may be infertile, you will have a special memorial and name in the new temple in the New Jerusalem (Isa. 56:4–7). Maybe God has prepared a special ministry for you through legal adoption of hard-to-place children rather than through fathering your biological children. God's promises are always valid and fulfilled in his time. After all, our children are merely loaned to us by God to continue his spiritual inheritance. Or perhaps you will find—even after much difficult soul searching—that God's plan for you is through some other ministry of Christian love in which you conform yourself to the likeness of Christ "to the praise of his glory" (Eph. 1:14).

Whatever it turns out to be, do not give up hope that God is even now working out his best plan for you.

Faith is now three years old, still very "floppy," but making excellent progress—thanks to her loving mother and the prayers of her family. She may never be an Olympic athlete, but she has brightened our lives and made her presence known throughout my hospital and our local area.

# Notes

1. The American Fertility Society, "How to Organize a Basic Study of the Infertile Couple," 1980.

2. D. R. Mishell and D. Avajan, *Infertility, Contraception and Reproductive Endocrinology* (Oradell, N.J.: Medical Economics Books, 1986), p. 258.

3. Ibid.

4. Fertility Society, p. 446.

5. Mishell.

6. Mishell, 446.

7. D.R. Dunihoo, *Fundamentals of Gynecology and Obstetrics* (Philadelphia: J.B. Lippincott Company, 1990), p. 558.

8. Ibid.

9. D. D. Federson, editor, *Abnormal Sexual Development: A Genetic and Endocrine Approach to Differential Diagnosis* (Philadelphia: W.B. Saunders, 1967).

10. B.H. Stewart, "Drugs as a cause and cure in male infertility," *Drug Therapy* 3 (April 1973):34. Also A.H. Ansari, R.G. Wieland, D.E. Klein, "Ciclomiphene citrate in the management of oligospermia," *Journal of Urology* 108 (1972):131.

11. T.M. Schellen and J.M. Beek, "The use of clomiphene treatment for male sterility," *Fertility and Sterility* 25 (1974):407.

12. D.F. Paulson, *et.al.*, "Clomiphene citrate: Pharmacologic treatment of hypofertile male," *Urology* 9 (1977):419.

13. A. Schachter, J.A. Goldman, and Z. Zuckerman, "Treatment of oligospermia with the amino acid arginine," *Journal of Urology* 110 (1973):311.

14. W.F. Hendry, *et.al.*, "Investigation and treatment of the subfertile male," *British Journal of Urology* 45 (1973):684.

15. B.H. Stewart and J. E. Montie, "Male infertility: An optimistic report," *Journal of Urology* 110 (1973):216.

16. Hendry.

17. V.B. Wilson and R.G. Bunge, "Infertility and semen nonliquefaction," *Journal of Urology* 113 (1975):509.

18. H. Lamensdorf, D. Compere and G. Begley, "Testosterone rebound therapy in the treatment of male infertility," *Fertility and Sterility* 26 (1975):409.

19. S.J. Silber, J. Galle and D. Friend, "Microscopic vasostomy and spermatogenesis," *Journal of Urology* 117 (1977):299.

20. L.G. Lome and L. Ross, "Varicocelectomy and infertility," *Urology* 9 (1977):416.

21. R. Ansbacher, K. Keung-Yeung and S.J. Behrman, "Clinical significance of sperm antibodies in infertile couples," *Fertility and Sterility* 24 (1973):305.

22. C.S. Lewis, *The Horse and His Boy*, (New York: MacMillan Publishing Co., 1954), p. 171.